GOING UP BEN NEVIS IN A BUBBLE CAR

(NEW WRITING SCOTLAND 18)

Edited by

MOIRA BURGESS
and
JANET PAISLEY

with Kevin MacNeil (Gaelic Adviser)

Association for Scottish Literary Studies

Association for Scottish Literary Studies
c/o Department of Scottish History, 9 University Gardens
University of Glasgow, Glasgow G12 8QH
www.asls.org.uk

First published 2001

British Library Cataloguing in Publication Data

A CIP record for this book is available
from the British Library

ISBN 0–948877–43–X

Published with assistance from

Typeset by Roger Booth Associates, Hassocks, West Sussex

Printed by Bell & Bain Ltd, Glasgow

CONTENTS

4   *CONTENTS*

INTRODUCTION

Here's New Writing Scotland 18 and we think it's a good one. That's what all the editors say, but oddly enough we have the opportunity to be all the more convinced of it this year. Delays in production – nothing to do with the editors, we swear – have meant that, in writing this introduction, we are looking at our selection some nine months after it was made, looking at *Going Up Ben Nevis in a Bubble Car* almost with the fresh eye of the casual reader who might pick it up in a bookshop. It stands the test. We're pleased that we chose as we did.

At the same time, this process does bring back the warm spring days (remember them?) during which we discussed the NWS submissions. Technically, we pulled them apart. Aesthetically, we considered whether they did the same to us. A few notes survive. 'Superbly stylish', reads one, and 'Made me greet', admits another, though in fact neither of these pieces made it through the final cull. (Did we mention that competition is fierce?) 'Great, loopy family story' made it, however. Can you spot it? So did the one in a Brummie accent. Yes, of course it's eligible – read the submission guidelines on another page with care – and we weren't obliged to bend the rules in order to include such an exceptional story. So did the Mars Bar one. Occasionally there's a piece which causes the editors to sit back, look at one another, and wish they had written it, and this is one of those.

Apart from such gut reactions, we think that, in the NWS tradition, this is a pretty balanced collection, representing stories and poems, English, Scots and Gaelic, city and country, men and women, gay and straight. Again, we didn't have to tweak our selection towards this result, and that gives us confidence for *New Writing Scotland 19*, when judging will be done 'blind'. (No authors' names on entries, see the guidelines again.) We reckon that our final selection for the next volume will still reflect the good writing coming to us from the widest possible range of sources, stylish and loopy and making us greet.

Moira Burgess
Janet Paisley

NEW WRITING SCOTLAND 20

Submissions are invited for the twentieth annual volume of *New Writing Scotland*, to be published in 2002, from writers resident in Scotland or Scots by birth or upbringing. Poetry, drama, short fiction or other creative prose may be submitted but not full-length plays or novels, though self-contained extracts are acceptable. The work must be neither previously published nor accepted for publication and may be in any of the languages of Scotland.

Submissions should be typed, double-spaced, on one side of the paper only and the sheets secured at the top-left corner. Prose pieces should carry an approximate word-count. You should provide a covering letter, clearly marked with your name and address. **Please do not put your name or other details on the individual works.** If you would like to receive an acknowledgement of receipt of your manuscript, please enclose a stamped addressed postcard. If you would like your submissions returned, you should enclose a stamped addressed envelope with sufficient postage. Submissions should be sent by **31 January 2002**, in an A4 envelope marked for my attention, to the address below. We are sorry but we cannot accept submissions by fax or e-mail.

Please be aware that we have limited space in each edition, and therefore shorter pieces are more suitable – although longer items of exceptional quality may still be included. A maximum length of 3,500 words is suggested. Please send no more than two short stories and no more than six poems.

Duncan Jones
Managing Editor, *New Writing Scotland*
ASLS
c/o Department of Scottish History
9 University Gardens
University of Glasgow
Glasgow G12 8QH
Tel: +44 (0)141 330 5309

Mark Baker

IN CAMERA

First I ken of it's the flash going off in my face – one, two, just like that. It's blinding. Wherever I look there's a black hole floating in front of me. Course, I ken right away what's happened.

Wee Davie's driving and I could throttle the stupid bugger on the spot. 'Stop a minute,' I tell him.

'What?'

Thick as mince.

'Stop the bloody car, will you?'

'But...'

I don't know if you've seen Davie lately, but he's grown one of those stupid pony tails. I grab it through the hole in the head rest and give it a tug. I'm in the back seat, you understand.

'If you don't stop right now I'll yank your bloody head off!'

So he jams the brakes on and we screech to a stop, leaving black lines on the tarmac.

'What is it?' says Morag. She's in the passenger seat and has turned round to look at me, the whites of her eyes orange in the light from the street lamps.

Who's Morag? Big Garvie's lassie. When we're planning the job he takes me on one side, puts his arm round me, and says he's starting her in the business; will I take her along. It's hard to refuse Garvie, and he's telling, not asking. I just nod, sagging under the weight of his paw, trying not to breathe that foetid breath of his.

Can you imagine going on a job like that with a bird with acne and a tee-shirt cropped so the stud in her navel keeps winking at you?

Anyhow, 'What is it?' she says.

'Michael Schumacher here's only triggered a bloody speed camera. Did you not see the flash?'

There's silence for a minute while that sinks in, then Davie says, 'S'nae problem. We've got false plates on, right?'

'You stupid bugger! Think I've got a false face on?'

'Eh?'

'I was looking out the back window, right at the bloody thing when it went off.'

'Why were you doin' that?'

'See if there was anyone behind, of course.' I skelp him one round the lug. 'Not that there was likely to be, the speed you were doing, you lead-footed moron. Did I not tell you just half a mile back to slow down?'

I sit fuming for a minute. Up till then things had gone sweet as anything – wire cut at Pete's Motors; nightwatchman tied to his chair, complete with brown underpants; safe peeled like it was an orange; two Gs in used notes sitting in the boot – and now this!

'What do we do now?' asks Morag.

'Well I'm not bloody leaving it. Think I want the law getting their snaps back from Boots and rolling up on my doorstep? Come on; let's have a look at the bloody thing.'

There's nobody about – it's four in the morning, you understand – so we back up and get out. It's a grey robocop sat on a square pole, nine or ten feet up. We're between street lamps, so the light's not so good, but I can see the wee windows on the front. I swear the thing's giving me the evil eye. To think my mugshot's in there, just waiting for the cops to drift by and pick it up.

It's by the end of a building, a warehouse or something, and next door there's a yard fenced off, with a hut in the middle – Tommy's Tool Hire it says. Right opposite there's a bank, and a chemist's with a neon sign advertising one-hour photos. A taxi rattles by, then it's quiet again.

'We could drive intae it,' says Davie, 'knock it over, right?'

I slap the pole and it kind of rings and shudders. 'What with? A chieftain tank?'

'My uncle got caught by one of these once,' says Morag.

Fascinating. Now's just the time to amuse ourselves with a few wee stories. 'And?' I say.

She catches my tone and shifts uncertainly on her feet. 'Well, apparently there's a hole near the top for ventilation, like. He squirted in some lighter fuel and set a match to it and ... boom!'

'Boom?'

'Aye. Boom.'

I turn to Davie. 'Go on. Up you go and take a look.'

'Why me? It's no' me it snapped.'

I skelp him again. 'Just do it.'

He shins up, wedging himself between the pole and the wall.

'He get away with it?' I ask Morag.

'Who?'

See what I've to put up with?

'Your uncle.'

She shakes her head. 'No. He knocked himself out falling on the pavement – you know, when it went "boom".'

Great.

'Cannae see a hole,' says Davie, who's at the top now, leaning round the front. Then he loses his grip and slithers down the pole, trying to stop himself with his hand on the brick wall.

'Ow, ow, ow,' he says, walking in a wee circle, bent over and clutching his hand.

'Idiot!'

'What about cutting it down with a chainsaw?' asks Morag.

'You got a chainsaw?'

'No. My Dad's got an angle-grinder though.'

'Where do you suggest we plug it in?'

Now she's looking up and down the street for a wall socket.

'Besides,' I say, 'anything like that would wake the whole bloody neighbourhood.'

'He's got a welding kit at the lock-up,' she says.

The lassie's wearing me down, but I daren't say too much, case she tells her Dad. 'Electric?' I ask.

'Gas.'

'Has he?' I look at her, thinking maybe this kid's not such a wash-out after all. 'Let's go and get it, then.'

Forty minutes later we're back. We park the Escort right by the camera, lay the bottles on the pavement, and I hook up the welding torch. Then, while my apprentices keep watch, I start cutting through the pole as high as I can reach. It's a wicked job to be doing in public – showers of sparks bouncing on the pavement, metal glowing bright orange, the reek of burning paint – but it's dead quiet and I've got as far as the fourth side before Morag calls out.

'Mind yourself! There's a car coming.'

We all duck down behind the Escort. I turn the oxygen off, but leave the acetylene on to keep the flame alight. I peer through the car windows and my blood turns to water in my veins. It's only a bloody panda car!

That's the trouble with working at night – the only folk about are taxi drivers, burglars, and cops.

Anyhow, the panda pulls up right opposite. I can smell Saughton in my nostrils – or maybe it's the whiff of hot metal – and there's a ringing in my ears like keys jangling. One of the coppers gets out and I'm wondering if we should make a run for it; but it's all right – he's only using the hole in the wall at the bank. He starts back to the car, but something must catch his eye, 'cause he looks across the road at us, then starts coming our way.

What to do? I look down at the torch in my hand. The wee flame's guttering, yellow and sulky. If I turn the wick up, get a blue cutting flame on it – take a brave bugger to face that. I can see it in my mind's eye – the blue serge burning, going black, the flesh scorching red behind it...

'Iain!'

It's the other copper, leaning out the car. The first one turns, sees him waving, runs back and climbs in. Then the blue light comes on, flickering on the brickwork and in the shop windows opposite, and they're off.

Ministers and policemen both – they can get the call any time.

Nobody says anything. We watch them disappear in the distance, and after a second to steady myself I set the flame again and finish lopping the thing off its pole. I see it start to lean, then all of a sudden it goes and whacks onto the pavement like an IRA bomb going off.

I cut the gas and it's so quiet I can hear the blood rushing in my ears. Morag and Davie are frozen like I've welded them to the pavement. I'm itching just to leave them there. Somewhere down the road a dog's barking, and a light's just flicked on in one of the flats opposite, over the chemist's.

'In the boot, quick!'

We load up robocop – thank Ford for hatchbacks, eh? – and the welding kit, then we're off too.

Back at the lock-up, we cut the thing open and there's a lot of wires and gubbins inside. None of it makes any sense to me.

'No camera,' says Morag, like she's some kind of expert on the things.

'How can there be no camera?'

'They move them around. Only a few boxes have a camera in at any one time.'

'Is that right?'

'My Dad told me.'

I'd already guessed that. I poke at a square black thing. 'What's this then?'

'The flashgun.'

'Oh.' It's a big sod, not like you'd use for happy snaps. 'And that?'

'The radar.'

Davie's nodding like he's an expert too. I skelp him one.

'Are you telling me all that was for nothing?' I say to Morag.

'Aye.'

'We could just have driven off?'

'Aye.'

'Shite!' I give the box a kick and send it skiting across the floor and into the wall. Then I look round for Dodgem Davie, just in time to see him scarper through the door.

Morag's not keen for her Dad to find robocop on the premises, you understand, so we put it back in the car, cart it along to the canal, and dump it. By now I've had enough, so I slip off to one of the all-night pubs down by the docks to refresh the parts. Executive stress – it's a terrible thing.

By seven I'm back at the flat and snug in my bed. I reckon I've earned my eight hours, but there's others think different, seemingly. I've barely shut my eyes before hammering breaks out in the hall like a carpenters' annual nail-driving competition. Guts churning, I open the door to pair of state-employed thugs armed with batons, who invite me to the cop shop at the West End for a wee chinwag. I slip on a tee-shirt and jeans, feeling less than keen on my new-found popularity.

I'm taken to the interview room and I'll admit it's a shock when I see Morag and Davie sitting there. Morag gives me a sort of sick smile and Davie reaches up with his hand like I'm going to hit him. There's two big lads on the door, with that sickening 'we've-got-you-bang-to-rights-this-time-laddie' smile they have. Then Inspector Meekison breezes in. I'm an old client of his.

'Sit down, laddie, sit down.'

My brain's having trouble with this. Was there film in the thing after all?

'Why'm I here?' I say, taking the seat facing his.

'Pay a visit to Pete's Motors last night, did you?'

'Where?'

'You heard.'

There's a smile playing on his lips I don't like the look of. Has someone clyped? I look at Morag again and she shakes her head, then at Davie and he kind of shrinks against the wall like a dog who's just come face to face with Rolf Harris. Was it him?

'Nobody's squealed, if that's what you're thinking.' Meekison's grinning at me, clearly enjoying some private joke.

I'm saying nothing.

'Like the flicks do you?'

I just shrug.

'Let's watch a wee video, shall we?'

I see there's a telly and a player set up in the corner. He reaches over and presses the button.

The picture's black and white, but there's no mistaking what it's showing. We're looking down from high up. There's a road on the left, a yard on the right with a building at the end, and a fence in-between. Some headlamps rush by, leaving white trails on the screen. There's a flicker and I see where robocop's hiding in the shadows by the building. Then a car backs up into shot and three people get out – a stunted youth, a girl with a tee-shirt too short to cover her midriff, and a bald-headed geezer…

'I don't believe it,' I say, shaking my head.

'You're never too old to be a film star, eh?'

The bastard's enjoying this.

'I'd've thought a pro like you would've checked round for video cameras.'

'Tommy's Tool Hire,' I say bitterly.

'Aye,' he says. 'Good enough for Jeremy Beadle, eh?'

He's killing himself, giving me a full-frontal of his fillings, but I'm not laughing. I'm seeing my old cell in 'A' hall again – three bunks, three stinking chamber pots, and 5,461 bricks. And I'm thinking of Garvie's Law, enforced by Garvie's Gorillas.

I go for Davie, get my hands round the bugger's throat, but the heavies in blue are too quick for me and drag me off him. I knew they would be.

Robert Barton

THE PROPOSAL

Lit's git married lass. Lit's leave this place tae nivir cum back. Ah'm gittin released nixt month an your due oot no long eftir.

Lit's live the gither, an dae away wi these hoaspitals. Ah'm an ol' man noo an Ah've been walkin these grun's an lookin at yon wa's fir mair years thin Ah wa'nt tae remembir.

Whit dae ye say lass? Ah'll take care ae ye. Ah'll gie ye yer pills oan time. Ah'll make sure ye've goat yir fags an a'. Ye'd save a loat mair money if ye wid jist switch tae tabacca mine ye. They filtered ur an awfy price. Ah'll wait fir ye lass. Ah've nae-where tae go 'cept that barn in Cleland thon big fairmers been kind enough tae lit me sleep in. Ay, Ah'm sleepin in a barn, and me wi four ae a faimily.

Ach naw, Ah cannae go back tae that hoose in Forgewood. They're no gie'n me a minutes peace nee'r they ur. Ah'm perse-cuted. Dae ye know, an this is withoot a word ae a lie, that any-where Ah go in that hoose they follow me? If Ah go tae make a cup ae tea then they're there, right above me. If Ah go intae the bedroom tae lie doon, where dae ye think they ur? Right above me. If Ah go tae use the toilet then Ah kin guarantee ye they'll be in theirs. Ah've complained an complained tae Ah'm blue in the face, it disnae make a blind bit ae difference whit Ah say. They're still gonnae keep at it.

So Ah'm sleepin in a barn. It's a bloody sin.

Dae ye know thit Ah've goat two grown lassies baith merried an Ah nivir knew a thing aboot it until eftir it wis a' o'er an done wi? An only then it wis a complete stranger thit telt me. Ah nivir goat tae see either ane ae ma lassies walkin doon that aisle. Ah'm the faither. Surely tae God it wis ma place tae walk doon that aisle wi them, wis it no? Ma eldest merried a protestant, aye, bit Ah should at least hiv goat tae take her tae the Registry Office should Ah no've?

So here Ah um lass. Not ane ae ma sisters ur brothers wid lift a finger tae help me. Ah don't talk tae oor Shona an oor Morag's no talkin tae me, she's in ane ae hir moods. Oor Pete's nivir wanted me an oor Joe's hoose is fu' or Ah ken he widnae hiv me oan the streets. C'mere, did Ah iver tell ye aboot him playin fitba?

The real killer is ma ain yins. That eldest lassie ae mine,

Rae, is bad – she's nae good tae her faither. Threw me oot ae her hoose so she did. Aye. Telt me tae 'git oot, an don't cum back'. Huh. Bit Ah'll tell ye this, see if Ah wis tae go tae hir hoose the morrow's morn wi a boatle ae Bacardi, she'd rip the haun aff me pullin me in so she wid. Ma uthir lassie's turnt oot no much bettir. Ailsa. She cin be a right dour yin at times. Ye've goat tae be loaded wi presents fur the weans tae be welcum in her hoose noo. Although she wisnae ayeways like that. The baith ae thum ur ayeways take, take, takin. It's ayeways 'gie me, gie me, gie me'. That Aisla is jist like ma sister Morag, ye nivir ken whit kind ae a mood ye'r gonnae git 'er in.

Ma eldest laddie noo, ach it's a sin. He's no weel. He's hid a hard life that boy, whit wi a' they uthir laddies ayeways pickin oan him. Widnae gie im a minutes peace nee'r they wid. Ah kin remembir seein them haudin im aff the bus an he'd be staunin there greetin fir 'is daddy. Ye'll ken they widnay be haudin 'im aff fir long wance they saw me cum running o'er tae git them. Ma biggest regret is that Ah nivir took im tae the boxin when 'e wis younger, teach im tae haun'l himsel. A' he does a' day is plays 'is records an watch the fitba oan the telly. He's Celtic daft so 'e is, jist like 'is faither.

Ma youngest son, noo that's a wee bastart. Ah said it fae the minute 'e wis born, 'that boy's no mine'. Sure whin Ah wis in the hoaspital 'is Muther couldnae wait tae git oot the hoose an' whoarin it up, goin tae thae bloody Ceilidh's an gittin drunk. Dae you know 'e's the only ane that's goat green eyes? There's naebuddy oan ma side wi thum. So you tell me where they cum fae. An 'e walks by me oan the street. Disnae want tae know me.

Ah remembir whin 'e wis jist a wee boy an him an 'is sister Aisla, who's only a year aulder, cum walkin t'wards me oan the street an 'e says tae her 'cum oan Aisla, ma granny says we're no tae talk tae him'.

Bit ye'll ken Aisla didnae walk by me though. No back then. No afore they turned hur against me. She wis ayeways a good lassie, hur faither's pet. She'd speak tae me. Used tae cum doon tae ma hoose in Forgewood an clean it fur me. Nun ae the rest ae thim wid've dun that. Made ma tea an rolled ma fags so she did. If evir anybuddy said onythin aboot hur faither, by God, hevin help thum. She'd be oot oan that street in a heartbeat, ur tearin doon yir door. Ho ho. Aye, that's ma lassie, the laddie Ah nivir hid.

Well there ye hiv it lass. That's ma faimily fir ye. Ah'm here a' these years an nary a visitur 'cept wance in a blue moon. Ah've bin placed undir loak an key in ward numbir seven. Ah've bin strapt tae a chair an hid electricity run through ma heid an still naebuddy cares.

D'ye know whit Ah dae cum visitin time when a' the faimilies cum? Ah pick masel up an Ah go walkin in yon wids. Aye, Ah luv these wids, naebuddy tae bother me. Jist me an the trees an the birds.

Ah luv walkin mine ye. Ach, Ah widnae pay the fares they're askin noo-a-days tae ride oan the buses. God gave me two strong legs. Ah've applied fir a disability pass anyways so Ah'll see how it goes.

So there ye hiv it. That's ma life laid oot afore ye. How aboot it? Whit dae ye say? Lit's git merried lass.

Iain Black

WED

The washed steps drying
to slender fingers clinging
clinging to
one piece of confetti
red and wet
like blood from a stone.

Tom Bryan

DEMOLITION

Rain shook the hard reeds, ripping the bracken to bits. Mud poured from the hills, rolling stones into swollen burns. Two men were knocking down an old croft from the inside. The walls were stained green and brown from damp and mould. They worked at the cladding.

Jimmy moved the crowbar in short bursts. Bits of plaster, wood and rock crumbled onto his scuffed boots, which crunched shards of plaster underfoot. The dust made a thin grey veil on the floor. The rain came in through missing slates and broken windows.

Kenny prised up the floorboards, most of them splitting where woodworm had riddled them into tiny feathered patterns like the tips of bird wings. Each effort brought more of the fusty smell of earth into the dust and debris. Both men worked smoothly, quickly; each pry of the crowbar hastened the end of the ruin.

Then, Jimmy made a clean slice with the crowbar and two objects leapt from the wall and landed in the slush and rubble at his feet. Jimmy looked at Kenny who looked back. 'Jesus Christ,' they said in unison and both leaned back, laying their tools down. 'Jesus Christ,' they repeated and both sucked in a breath and began to roll a cigarette each. At their feet were two glistening objects, taller than either of the men: a black war shield and a ceremonial war mask bristling with large garish feathers of some exotic bird. Jimmy and Kenny stood back, fingering their cigarettes. 'Mother of God,' said Kenny, crossing himself and stubbing the cigarette out on the plaster-covered floor.

The rain pelted down while four faces – two living and two freshly resurrected – wondered at this thing happening in another century far from the dusty African veldt where great lions still sleep in the sun, untroubled by cold Lochaber rain.

Ron Butlin

SAILOR'S MOTHER

Sailor's mother had straightened up too suddenly from bending over the sink – the green kitchen walls were buckling in and out, the floor ribbing to waves that all but knocked the feet from under her. She grabbed the rim of the stainless steel sink. That bastarding son of hers should have been up long past. His breakfast, his dinner, his clothes, his boots, his noise and mess: the day would become his from the first rush of water in the pipes and the *thud-thud* of his size-twelves on the stairs. The battery wall-clock, 'A Present from Ayr Where There's All the Time in the World', showed ten-thirty. Him and his sore head would be appearing any minute. She'd knocked earlier like he'd asked, and now his tea was cold and slicked over – a waste of good sugar. Nine, he'd said. A job at Dyer's Cottage, he'd said. One last try: she made her way up the stairs, pushed open the door and shouted.

No response. That window hadn't been opened in weeks: the bed-smell, the sweat, beer, fags and God only knows what else about turning her stomach. The scrub of red hair, red beard, freckles and broken veins were all she could see of him. His shoulder stuck out from under the blanket, she shook it till he grunted, then shook again.

'Come on, Davey. It's way past ten.'

'Aye?'

'Ye lump ye. Past ten, I'm saying.'

'Aye.'

More like a breathing between his teeth than speaking. He'd be going back to sleep any second.

'You were to be at Dyer's Cottage an hour past. Man'll be waiting.'

'Aye, I'll be down.'

'You'd better.'

Sailor's mother stood up from leaning over the bed and again felt her legs all but giving way. She took good hold of the wooden headboard and stayed where she was while the room steadied itself around her. The view out the window blurred in and out of focus; through the gap in the curtain she could see a dozen fields slithering together into a heap of yellows and greens, until they separated again into one field each of rape and grass. Douglas Hill had a dozen tops to it and seemed like a hand of cards being riffled towards her and away, keeping time, so it felt, with the vein pulsing at the side of her head.

When the room had settled down to its usual midden of clothes and underwear on the floor, an oiled saw at an angle against the wall, and rabbit snares and netting and waders and a shotgun barrel next to the wardrobe, she glared down at the nigh-on-fifty-years-of-running-after that had already gone back to snoring wetly on its pillow. Another job lost.

Sailor had been thirty-four when he'd returned after ten years in the Merchant Navy. No letter, no phone call to let them know he'd be arriving. Not a word – their only warning was the sound of someone barging their way into their front lobby.

'Whae the hell's that?' her old man had called out above the western he was watching at near full-volume; he'd have been expecting nobody much, like the minister or Tod Wilson to see if he was for a walk up to Stuart's farm for eggs. Anyone else would come to the back door; poor Tod hadn't the sense to know any better. Sailor's mother had nearly dropped her cup with the shock as the living-room door opened with no sound of a greeting coming through first.

And there he'd stood: blue jeans, white vest, brown leather jacket and a tan to match, but for his fair skin. All five foot ten of him looking pleased and awkward as he stood half in the room and half out. Beard like a hedge needing seen to.

'You're back then?' A jerk of the head from her old man who'd no intention of getting to his feet, that was clear.

'Davey, son!'

She'd rushed over, she was holding him tighter than she'd done since he was a boy, and trying not to cry; behind her the Indians were still whooping, their ponies' hooves still hammering and thundering round the wagon train. It had been eight-thirty when he'd come in the door; a summer's evening, and the light outside so clear it made darkness seem only a memory of winter.

She'd given him the biggest fry-up ever through in the kitchen while her old man sat at his end of the table with a cup of tea. For the next hour they heard about China, Madagascar, the Pacific, so large he'd forgotten what dry land looked like, and the north coast of Greenland where the creak and muffled boom of the ice-floes drifting past sounded like the ship breaking up.

Then it was round to the pub. She'd waited up for them, making a start on his clothes. There'd been a lock-in in his honour, her old man boasted when the two of them came back. Davey's plans already coming loud-voiced through the door in front of him: renting the low field from Stuart, sheep, hens, bees, pigs, raspberry canes, a boat and night-lines for the loch, a van and tools for repair work. Tod Wilson and Wee Cammie had trooped in after with a carry-out that needed carried between them. A late night, and it was she who had to speak up about their beds with the daylight already well started behind the closed curtains and the living-room a grown man's mess of smoke and crushed cans. They'd woken Tod, and Wee Cammie said he'd see him home. Davey'd managed upstairs himself, second try.

Back in the kitchen Sailor's mother carried on with the labelling: two dozen honey, two dozen jam. Not a lot, but better than nothing. They honey was for selling, the jam they'd have on bread, rolls, scones, toast, by itself, in puddings, cakes till it got used. Five jars more and she'd put on the kettle so it would be boiled in time for her finishing.

She was on her third last label, which wouldn't stick straight but seemed to take a jerk to itself each time she pressed it onto the glass, when she heard someone's knock at the front door. The jar nearly jumped out of her hand: and that would have been £1.50 turned to stickiness and smashed glass on the floor. She put the jar, slow-motion and double-handed, onto the formica worktop, then held her breath and listened, and waited. Front door was where the grief came in: Social Security, police, anything official, anyone after somebody or something – usually that bastarding waste of space upstairs in its bed.

Another knock. She was standing next to the low electric humming from the Ayr clock, a never-ending grumble she'd learnt to put up with; she'd always wanted an old-fashioned wag-i-the-wa' that struck out every tick with a clear back-and-forward swing of its pendulum. She'd wanted, so she never got. Who did? It was nearly eleven, too late for the post. There were footsteps on the side path: the bad news was coming round to the back.

A blur of tallness was suddenly darkening the pebbled-glass of the kitchen door, a knuckle was rapping the woodwork. Whoever it was would be trying to peer in soon enough: she hadn't the strength to get herself through into the sitting-room out of sight. She went to the door and opened it.

'Sorry to bother you, but is this where Sailor lives?'

A waxed jacket, green cords and an apologetic-looking smile –

the man from Dyer's Cottage, had to be.

'He sleeps here.'

'Oh?'

On second glance, the waxed jacket looked short in the arms and the cords concertina-ed below the knees: either very well off, or no better than he should be.

'Let you down, has he?'

'I was expecting him two hours ago. Supposed to be bricking up a loose bit of wall. Getting kind of urgent. I'm in the old place beyond the farm.' The man pointed up the road with a hand that was obviously no working hand, and never had been.

At that moment Sailor's mother heard the water in the pipes and knew the *thud-thud* would be coming after.

'Why don't you come in? He's just getting himself ready.'

Fifteen minutes later the man from Edinburgh who'd bought Dyer's Cottage to do up for weekends, had also bought two jars of honey and two of jam. He couldn't stop thinking about his back wall: he could picture the large stones that had loosened overnight and now rocked at a touch like milk-teeth. It had rained heavily all the previous day so he'd not been surprised when Sailor hadn't appeared. Today, with the dry, some of the larger stones were rolling free; here and there the wall above them was cracking, threatening to give way. He sat drinking tea he didn't want while picturing to himself the uninterrupted view there would soon be from his garden into his kitchen, bathroom and back bedroom when the wall finally collapsed. Which might very well be happening at that precise moment: meanwhile he was being kept perching on the edge of the kitchen chair, gripping the edge of the kitchen table and politely listening to Sailor's mother telling him, at length, what a lazy so-and-so her son was. The man was aye letting folk down, she was saying, and it was a wonder folk kept asking him; his father had been a good worker, in his way.

'If only Davey'd met a good girl who'd have made something of him, but what lass is going to stop in the village? What's she to stop for? It's brains or bairns nowadays; they're either left the place for something better or stayed and got themselves hitched by the time they're eighteen. Sailor they might call him, but he's missed that particular boat long since.'

The man from Edinburgh couldn't remain in his seat a second longer. He picked up his Tesco bag with its dull-clinking of jars and was about to make his apologies before leaving. But Sailor's mother was too quick for him, and already heading towards the stairs:

'I'll take a stick to the good-for-nothing, you wait here.'

*

The three pounds she'd got for the honey was in her money tin and staying there. Once the lino was swept, it would be time to start cooking. Was she going to give him yet another talking to or just bang down his dinner and say nothing. What did it matter anyroad? Nothing ever changed, him least of all. She'd done this floor a thousand times, and here she was – still doing it. Trying to talk sense into that sack of stupidity was no different. These days she seemed to sweep harder than ever, and the floor seemed dirtier than ever: bits of egg-shell, onion skins, a tea-bag, a hank of sheep's wool. The brush kept sticking in the corners, banging itself against the skirting-board like a live thing. As she lifted the metal dust-pan for emptying, it clattered against the oven door. Her head swam and she staggered a couple of steps like she was going to faint. She put her free hand on the cooker to give herself a bit ease. Yes, she'd save her breath; she'd wasted more than enough on that do-nothing disgrace who went around the village dressed like a burst bin-bag.

Sailor's mother placed the dust-pan against a leg of one of the kitchen chairs to make brushing it easier. 'Think someone'd invent longer handles,' she heard herself say out loud. 'But it won't be that burst bin-bag, anyroad!' She laughed. That was her Davey, and no mistake. The more she thought of him looking like that the more she laughed.

She was still laughing when she stood up after the last of the sweeping; there was a sudden rush of dizziness. She reached for the kitchen-table to steady herself. But there was no table anymore. No table, no chairs, no worktops, no cooker. Instead, to Sailor's mother it seemed the entire kitchen had turned into an almost blinding light: she had only to reach forwards to grasp hold of the brightness all around her. Not until the very end did she sense the darkness she was falling into…

Sailor had had a good day. After a late lie-in he'd slipped out the front door and gone round to Tod's for a hair of the dog. The two of them then went to check the rabbit snares he'd set the day before: two full-grown ones apiece. Next, down to the nets in the bridge pool: three salmon and a trout. They'd built a fire in Corbie Wood, skinned, gutted and cooked one of the rabbits while finishing off Tod's bottle. Tod was a good man to pass the day with – not a great talker. As the fire burnt itself out to red and grey ash Sailor lay in the grass staring up into the late afternoon sky. His ten years away at sea were more and more like memories of someone else's life, not his. When he'd gone ashore with the others after weeks on end at sea, it had been a mad scramble to get drunk and laid. All he could remember now were windowless rooms, beds with curtains pinned up round them, and that afterwards he'd always felt depressed until he'd got back onboard. Since returning home he'd never left the village, even for a day.

Much later, with the cash from Michael at the hotel for the fish and rabbit, they'd had themselves a really good night.

It was after eleven when Sailor tacked his way home down the middle of the empty main road. There was no light in the cottage. No sense in waking up his mother by clattering through the whole house, so he went in the front. He closed the door behind him, locked it for the night and began to climb the stairs up to bed. By tomorrow's breakfast the job at Dyer's Cottage would be ancient history; he would tell her he was going to spend the morning digging potatoes. He'd bring her back a good sackful. Fresh lifted, they'd be at their best. She loved them, he knew that.

Maoilios Caimbeul

BRISEADH NA CLOICHE

Thog thu còmhnaidh, a ghlòir,
'nam chridhe
's gun fhios a'm gu robh thu ga thogail.
O iongantais neo-fhaicsinnich an spioraid!
Am measg a' chlàbair 's a' phuill
bha do làmhan
ro gheal
ag ullachadh an làraich,
        ni do-thuigsinn
        nach gabh tuigsinn
        nach gach creidsinn.

A! Tha a' chlach seo fhathast
gad chumail a-mach,
brùid mhòr far am bu chòir staran bhith.

Bris i, a ghlòir,
ged a bhiodh e goirt, bris i
na bloighdean beaga
gus am bi slighe rèidh ann, mu dheireadh,
dhad chois
agus cluinnidh mi fuaim do choise air a' ghreabhail
agus bidh mi le fiamh 's le uamhann
a' feitheamh glòir do theachd.

        'S bidh an taigh a bha falamh
        làn de àirneis iongantach,
        làn, làn, làn,
        agus 'na neoni.

THE BREAKING OF THE STONE

You built a dwelling, glory,
in my heart,
although unaware you were building it.
O invisible marvel of the spirit!
In the midst of the mire and the mud
your hands
most white
were preparing the site
        something inexplicable
        inscrutable
        unbelievable.

Ah! The stone is still there
keeping you out,
a great brute of a stone where a path should be.

Break it, glory,
although painful, break it
in smithereens
until there is a smooth path, at last,
for your foot
and I will hear the sound of your feet on the gravel
and with awe and dread
I'll await your glorious arrival.

        And the once empty house
        will be full of amazing furniture,
        full, full, full,
        and it will be nothing.

A' BHOITEAG

1.

Nam bhoiteag
ann an ùir an t-saoghail,
bidh mi, saoilidh mi, a' faireachainn blàths
mar gum biodh làmh ga mo shuathadh.
Uaireannan os mo chionn
bidh mi a' faireachdainn coiseachd
gun fhosadh
gun lasadh,
ach aon latha
mar gun dùisgeadh rudeigin an ùir
chaidh mo shadail suas
agus loisg soillse gun ainm mo chùl.

B'fheàrr leam gun robh mi
air ais anns an ùir
a' faireachdainn na corraig caoin
gam bhuaireadh
gam shuathadh
le eòlas an t-solais àird, àrd os mo chionn.

2.

Faodaidh a' bhoiteag fhèin
cuideam an dè fhaireachdainn.

Faodaidh a' bhoiteag fhèin
blàths na grèin fhaithneachadh.

THE WORM

1.
A worm
in the soil of the world,
I sometimes, I think, feel a warmth
as if a hand were stroking me.
Sometimes above me
I feel footsteps
without pause,
ceaseless,
but one day
as if something disturbed the soil
I was thrown upwards
and an unknown glow burnt my back.

I wish I was
back in the soil
feeling the gentle finger
agitating me
stroking me
with the knowledge of the distant light, high above me.

2.
Even the worm
can feel the weight of the god.

Even the worm
can recognise the heat of the sun.

J.J. Calvin

FIFTEEN MINUTES

I want it.
Deep in my bones there's a pain nagging for relief. I'm due it.

I need it.
Others tell me it's simply a question of self belief. I have it.

I hear it.
Beckoning a siren call that urges me to stake my claim. I'll heed it.

I fear it.
This, my end, once I teach them not to mock my name. I'll do it.

I stoke it.
This burning Hell which cancels all that's gone before. I eat it.

I stroke it.
This means of retribution, a hundred scores or more. I'll clear it.

I see it.
This final one reserved for me once the deed is done. I'll take it.

I'll be it.
For fifteen minutes. Now I lift and cock the loaded gun. I aim it.

Stewart Conn

KOSOVO

i   Milena

She lies at the edge of the pines,
black hair drifting over her face,
a silver earring sparkling;
alongside her mother and two brothers,
one's arm bent over his forehead
as if still cowering from the bombs.

Among the rubble, in a childlike hand,
poems to a boyfriend: *Your Milena*
still loves you. If only you knew
how much I suffer. I feel my wounds so
I don't know if I can still kiss you.
In capitals in English, again *I LOVE YOU.*

These lines and what they proclaim
all that remain as her body is loaded
on a dumper-truck and taken away.

ii   The Hunt by Night

Figures run headlong through the forest
till all are brought down. At dawn
a great exhalation shrouds the marshes,
the meadows nearby. The beasts of the field
long since gone, the fowls of the air taken flight.

iii   Ogre

We see on the screen daily
his puffy cheeks and white hair,
a man who has a price on his head.

To think he rises each morning,
does his ablutions like any other,
and passes out to the mundane air.

Disconcerting to have no sign: a malign
bubbling under the skin, or an insect
crossing the eyeball of the living man.

iv   **Hope**

Think: in the depth of the forest
a source of light – only to discover
a tiny songbird, its plumage on fire.

v   **The well**

Arc-lights blazing they detect rotting
shapes, the stench unbearable: no
grapnel could pull them out without
fear of dismemberment.
                            Suggested:
Rope a gypsy, drop him down ...

vi   **This land**

              – our birthright, who
religiously plough its hectares,
teach our children its anthem.

              – should be ours
in restitution, our forefathers
having been put to the sword.

vii   **The inheritors**

One dig unearths rows of corpses,
all male, heads aligned to the north;

Another, on the far side of the knoll,
centuries-old skeletons without skulls.

An eye for an eye, a tooth for a tooth.

viii   'What can I do for Kosovo...?'

'I cannot offer hope, far less bring
loved ones back from the dead: so what
do I do?' Then it came to her: 'I can sing.'

A fund-raising concert ended
with a radiant rendering of some
of Bach's most sublime cantatas.

ix   Exile

The school razed
to the ground, his
singing-master garrotted,

he no more dreams
of returning than
entering a roaring fire.

Far less of waiting
till his God holds
sway over theirs.

Each day he practises
to develop the muscle
cavities round his throat

x   Envoi

A new millennium
begun: lavish parties,
rapturous tolling of bells.

Here, the dominant
sound still the thud
of the gravedigger's spade.

Ian Crockatt

from: *Love Sequence*

5.

And love keeps intervening like a referee,
getting thumped but pushing in again,
insisting on being the no-man's land we
score between us after each offensive;

while the parents of this poppy-spattered boy
beg him to throw in the towel but over
the top he goes, no more than their big bruised boy
blundering into a world they'll never know;

and this minister fluttering his hanky
over our stretchered lives – while bullets
snub their noses on pavements and bone –
until some final whistle is blown.
And what shall lovers do? Stripped to the blood-
stained skin am I naked enough for you?

Anna Crowe

PARABLE

Dying in Jarrow, Bede
held up three fingers, and blessed
his brothers with all he owned: a length
of linen, incense, a box of pepper.

Go home and spread the cloth;
set bread upon the table, fill
the pepper-mill, a jug of water;

and when you have lit the candles,
see how your cupboards full of things
retreat into the shadows;

as you bite into a peppercorn
and fragrance bursts upon your tongue,
it will come to you in a rush how less
is more, and little much.

Penelopeanne Dagleish

PERSEPHONE AT HALLOWEEN

Gazing into the orange ball
Of the pomegranate,
The woman sees she has eaten
Too many seeds again.

She sighs over the repeated mistake.

Her gazing finds the ring-giver –
Next year's pumpkin lantern.
(A candle shines through the sockets
Of her last husband's eyes.)

It would be wearing, unbearable,

If it were not for the children
Gobbling sweets, cracking nuts,
Bubbling with the last few apples.
They laugh behind the masks

She discarded. Her faces fit perfectly now.

Robert Davidson

HIS SISTER'S HANDS

He was hurt and distraught and so he rocked
in his chair. His sister, who was a rock,

clasped his shoulders till the worst of it passed.
But all his heart and mind were in the past

once more. His sister put the kettle on
for tea. By now his daughter would be on

her way. His sister dusted here and there.
At eleven she had spoken to their

parents, lifting the phone on the first ring.
He could not speak himself. He turned his ring

around his finger over and again.
His sister answered the damned phone again

and said, 'He can't speak to you at present.
So sorry, I'll tell him you called.' Present

as it had always been, his sister's will
made him nearly strong and held his own will

fast. 'My heart is breaking,' he said, his hands
clutching at themselves while his sister's hands

went round him with their touch that never failed,
that caught and held the pieces as they fell.

Judy Delin

SOMETHING TO SUCK

So now I'm on a Northern train.
She leaned towards me
as soon as I sat down.
Fifty, warmly clad, and
burrowing thermos-drink and sandwiches
out of a tartan bag.

Do you want something to suck?

As if that's what you do on trains.
The only way to travel.
I accept a boiled sweet,
and she sits back, satisfied.
We sit and suck in comfortable silence.

Yes oh yes
How could you have known
how dry my mouth
and how much in need of sweetness.

Anne Donovan

MRS CLOUD SAYS

Mrs Cloud says to give out the milk don't spill a drop. Mrs
Cloud says today is Friday and tomorrow is Saturday and the
nex day is Sunday and we've all to go to mass at ten o clock.
says blessed are the pure of heart.
I don't go to mass at ten o clock.

Mrs Cloud's hair is white and fuzzy like cotton wool balls.
Mrs Cloud teaches us to draw leafs. They are all kind of leafs.
They are ash and oak and sick a more leaf. She shows us how
you can tell the leafs by their shape. The sick a more leaf is
my favourite but the oak is easy to draw.

Mrs Cloud wears red shoes. She gives me a blue star.
Jamie says Mrs Cloud is a   jamie is a big boy.
Mrs Cloud says a prayer and we learn it off by heart. Mrs
Cloud says blessed
Jamie is a big boy Jamie sayed a bad word.
I told mrs Cloud she says you dirty girl wash out your mouth
with soap and water.
I don't like Mrs Cloud.
Mrs Cloud hit me with the ruler. She hurted my hand. it
went red.

And the nex day is Sunday I don't go to mass
at ten o'clock I go to the wood. I see the leafs. There are all
kind of leaf. They are brown and curly and they rustle.
I can't tell which is the sick a more leafs.

Mrs Cloud says two twos is four four fours is eight. She
wears red shoes I have a red ribbon there is a red mark. I can
jump in without missing. Please miss may I give out the milk?
She says why did you miss mass on Sunday? Please miss I did
not miss mass on Sunday.

Mary gives out the milk and don't spill a drop. The milk is
sour. We drink our milk.

The statue of Our Lady has stars round her head she is the queen of Heaven. Blessed virgin. Immaculate conception. Conceived without sin. Blessed are the pure.

Jamie says it's an oak tree. In the wood.
God is everywhere He can see everything. In the wood.

We fold our arms when Father Reilly comes he is the parrisht priest he is blessed. He says God is a spirit and God is Our father who art in heaven. He shows us his fingers they are blessed. Mrs Cloud says thank you Father. We stand up.

There is a scab on my knee don't pick it. I can't help it.

I can jump in without missing and I sing we are three wee gallus girls sailing out to sea and if you want the fairest one you'll have to pick
on
pick on
me.

Bless me father for I have sinned. This is my first con fession. Mrs cloud says to tell the priest all your sins so you can be wiped clean. Mrs Cloud shows us to draw a stamen on the flower. There is no flowers in the wood. They are all kinds of leaf. I feel the leafs on my knees. They are stones under the leafs. They hurted my knees. Mrs cloud says God is every-where. Jamie says a bad word Jamie is a big boy. Mrs Cloud says you dirty girl.

And tomorrow is Saturday and you've all to go to   don't say chapel say church. And why because we've all to make our first con fession. Bless me father. There is flowers in the chapel for Our Lady she is our mother. Mrs Cloud shows us to draw a stamen. Jamie is an altar boy he helps the priest but his fingers are not blessed.

Me father for I have Tell me your sins.
I missed mass that is a mortal sin. Why did you miss mass.
A big boy made me.
No one can make you.
God made me. God is everywhere he sees everything. In the
wood. My knees are sore they rub on the stones. An ee
jaculation is a short prayer. Jesus mary and Joseph I give you
my heart and my soul. God is merciful. He forgives us our
sins.
He pulls my hair he says look I'll show you I don't want to
Look
is a verb is a doing word.

A noun is a naming word. She says to write a noun in your
book. I don't know the name. Of the word. And the doing.
It.

Is cold in the wood the cold air. Jamie hurted me. Mrs Cloud
says an adjective is. A describing word. Jamie is a bad boy.
Bad is an adjective. Jamie done a bad thing. Mrs Cloud says
it's did not done. It is done.
Blessed is an adjective. Blessed are they
who know not
what they done.

Moira Duff

GOING UP BEN NEVIS IN A BUBBLE CAR

It's like swaying in a raindrop from a tree.
Staring in their eyes, and them in
ours all the crawling thousands of
feet up this thread. There's Loch Linnhe
a million miles away. Fortwilliam's a snapshot from
Sound of Music. 'Doppelmayer
gondolas,' it says, 'Do not lean out.' 'In
case of breakdown follow operator's
instructions.' Do we
cut the cord and sledge in some
ghastly pill bottle, me clutching your
trousers and him clawing in my hair?
'Use loudspeaker,' it says. I'll
reverberate deafly as the
hills come alive with my calls and screams,
dangling arm, pants elastic, front door
keys, all my lipstick upside-down.

Bill Duncan

THE VILLAGE STREET, HOUSE NUMBER 14

Space of a missing door
framing a cold moon.
Behind a broken grate
the black of a dead fire.

A wind blows
through the bones of the house
between ruined stones
echoing an old song.

Matthew Fitt

FORGOTTEN AIRFIELDS O
WEST CENTRAL BOHEMIA

the wund scarts at the birks
boys scutter wi a puck on the frozen lochan

the pilot has nae cigarette tae licht
she cups his hauns wi hers
an tells him it'll soon be summer

then wi a gleg airm,
he ruggs awa the chocs
haps his een wi sopwith-camel goggles
feels his hert skelp faster in his chist

she bides by the skoda
smoorin the cauld intil her wi a scarf
an smiles

she kens where he's gaun an hou far

heid boued in the micro-licht cockpit,
he hirples the plane twiced
roon the roch ploued field o hajany airbase
then wi a gesture
mair puggled than crabbit
sneds the ile-flow tae the engine

she reads an unnerstauns the scunner in his face
but gledly retrieves her goggie's haun
an drives him hame throu the sub-zero winter glaur

thirty thoosan feet
abinn the jeel-cauld west czech forests
an arra-heid o soviet bombers
dinnles dour anthems amang the altocumulus

Moira Forsyth

COLLECTING THE WATER
for Stuart and Susan Chisholm

Behind the hills November light
holds all the radiance of summer gone.
Glen Cannich blazes red and gold and green
as you dip the bottle in the burn
fill it with water clear as glass
and raise it to the sun.

I click the shutter, catch the second as it goes.

All this to bless the downy head
of a baby born to flourish
in a dry and southern soil
with the coolness of the north
the mist that veils the hills
the stillness of the loch
the translucent dusk that falls
on the land that gave him breath.

Pete Fortune

MA BEST FREIN KENNY

Ma best frein Kenny. We aye gae out for beer thegither on Friday nichts. A whein o pints in the *Ship*, an if we're up til it, haufs in sum late nicht bar. Mebbe ane o thon fancy bits whaur aa the young fowk gaither. We aye hae a guid blether Kenny an me, but the ither nicht he wes in gey queer fettil.

'Aa richt, whit's up?' A asked. 'No been gettin on wi Linda?'

'A wish it wes that straicht-forrit,' he replied, shakin his heid.

A wes juist luikin at him, sayin nocht.

'The fuckin cairrie-on A've been landit in at hame,' he said. 'It's like sumthin straicht out the tabloids.'

'Sounds like fun. Tell me about it.'

'We've been haein a bit trubbil wi the lassie that babysits,' he said.

'Whit kind o trubbil?'

'Weill, ti stert wi, an awfu cairrie-on wi the weans.'

'Nou *that* daesna sound like fun.'

'Ay, ye're tellin me. Oniewey, it wes sumthin wee Jenny cam out wi ane efternuin, sumthin aboot Wendy that babysits. A didna like the sound o it.'

'Ay?'

'The wean luiked feart – ken? – said it wes a saicret, but A suin got it out o her.'

'Whit wes gaun on?'

'Thay war playin sum queer gemm. Doctors an nurses wad ye believe?'

'Is that whit the wean said?'

He noddit his heid. 'Wendy wes gettin the weans ti examine her. Ye ken?'

'Examine her?' A repeated.

'Ay, bluidy examine her. A'll spare ye the gruesum details. Mak ye seik.'

'Christ aamichty. Whit age is this Wendy?'

'Fifteen. Ye've met her. She wes thare whan ye cam ti the houss for a drink ane nicht. Her frae alang the road, the lassie wi the legs up ti her thrappil.'

'The lass that wes drinkin the Beck's? Near suikin the tap aff the bottle?'

'That's the ane.'

'She's only fifteen?'

He noddit. 'Ay. Sleekit wee bitch she is tae.'

He wes mebbe smilin, A'm no shuir. Mebbe he wesna.

'Whit ir ye daein about it?' A asked.

'Weill, A haed a word wi Wendy. Tellt her straicht – she wadna be babysittin for us again – an warned her ti stey weill awa frae the weans.'

'Is that aa ye've duin about it?'

'How dae ye mean? Whit dae ye expek me ti dae?'

'Weill, her mither an faither should be tellt, if no the law. Christ, thare's a case thare for fetchin the polis in, shuirly?'

'Na. A wantit ti leave it alane, for the sake o the weans. Thay've been throu enough. A mean, A didna e'en tell Linda the fou storie. Sae the polis... na, A dinna think sae. Thay're as weill kep out o it. Thare juist didna seem the need.'

'*Didna seem the need?* She must be aff her heid this Wendy lassie. Christ sake Kenny, A mean... lissen, A bet ye'd fetch the polis if it haed been a young bloke gaun on that wey.'

'Weill, it wad be deifferent if it wes a fellie.'

'How? In whit wey deifferent?'

'Cam on. If it wes sum manky wee tyke wi a big tadger... weill o course it wad be deifferent. That wad be sumthin else aathegither.'

'Yer actin kind o glaikit, Kenny. Tell me, whit age ir yer weans?'

'Jenny's seiven an the boys ir fower nou.'

'Ye hae ti tak heed o the damage. Thare's nae wey o tellin whit kind o effeck this micht hae haed on thaim.'

He wes shruggin his shouders. 'A'm content ti juist let it rest.'

'Sae whit did she say whan ye confronted her?'

'Denied it o course. Acted aa hurt an innocent, said it wes aa a pack o lees.'

'Ye're shuir enough it is true thou?'

'Weill, Jenny's a bit young ti make that sort o thing up, is she no?'

'Ay, A suppose she is. Puir wee lassie...'

'Thare's mair ti it thou. Wendy's turnt the heat back on me.'

'How dae ye mean?'

'Weill, it seems her faither haed wanted ti ken why she wesna babysittin for us onie mair. Wantit ti ken if thare wes a reason.'

'An whit did she say?'

'Ach, she sterted ti greit an that made him suspeicious. He

gaed her an awfu time o't an in the enn she cam out wi a load
o shite.'

'How dae ye ken aa this?'

'A heard it aa frae him. Loud an bluidy clear. She tellt her
faither she wesna comin back ti babysit for us kis A'd made a
pass at her.'

'A pass at her?'

'Ay. Said A'd becam owre forrit wi her ane nicht whan
Linda wesna thare. Tryin ti kiss her, grabbin at her tits, haun
up the skirt...'

'Christ aamichty, did her faither confront ye wi aa this?'

'Ay. He turnt up at the houss rantin an ravin like an eidiot.
It wes fuckin terrifyin, speciallie in front o Linda. He said he wes
thinkin on phonin the polis. That, or mebbe rippin ma heid aff
ma shouders insteid.'

'Whit did ye dae?'

'Kep a guid distance, nae fear. He's a big fearsum-luikin
bastart.'

'About the allegations thou?'

'Denied it o course,' he replied, 'A denied it.'

'Did ye no gie him the truith thou? Tell him whit his lassie
haed been up ti wi the weans?'

'Na. He wes gaun fuckin mental as it wes. If A'd said thon
ti him, A dout A wadna be here the nicht ti tell ye about it. A
sweir ti God, he wes like a man dementit. But na, A juist denied
it aa. Said A'd been naewhaur near his dochter.'

Then Kenny wes up an joukin tiwards the toilet, gropin his
wey atwein aa the young fowk gaithert aroun the juke box. He
wes mebbe smilin, A'm no shuir. Mebbe he wesna. He stopped
an haed a bit blether an a laugh wi ane or twa lassies, then he
disappeart inti the toilet for his pish.

Ma best frein Kenny.

Anne Frater

OIDHCHE REOITE

Nuair a bha an t-adhar buidhe
's nach robh dorchadas ann
's nach robh fuaim na mara nam chluaisean
neo fàileadh ceò na mòine nam chuinnlean
cha do smaoinich mi oirbh
's fios a'm nach biodh ann
ach ionndrainn gun fheum.

Ach dh'fhuirich sibh far an robh sibh
a' feitheamh rium.

Agus air oidhche reòite
's mi air teiche bho sholuis a' bhaile mhòir
chì mi sibh a' deàlradh
mar a bha sibh riamh
's sibh a' cuir fàilt' air an nighean stròdhail
a thill.

A FROSTY NIGHT
When the sky was yellow
and there was no darkness
and no sound of the sea to be heard
or peat-smoke to smell
I didn't think of you
knowing it would be
a useless yearning.

But you stayed put
waiting for me.

And on a frosty night
now I've left the city lights
I can see you shining
as you always were
as you welcome the prodigal daughter
who returned.

COMHAIRLE

Nan canadh tu nach tigeadh tu
thuiginn
's chan iarrainn ort a' chòrr.
Ach thig thu
agus falbhaidh tu
a' fàgail mì-chinnt is teagamh
às do dhèidh.

Na bi cho modhail
mura h-eil thu gam iarraidh
's gu h-àraid ma tha!

ADVICE

If you said you wouldn't come
I'd understand
and I wouldn't ask any more.
But you come
and you go
leaving uncertainty and doubt
in your wake.

Don't be so polite
if you don't want me
and especially if you do!

MÌ-CHINNT

Mi coiseachd tarsainn air an fhadhail,
mo shùilean air mo cheann-ùidh;
's gun fhios 'am a bheil a' mhuir
a' tionndadh
gam chur a choiseachd
air gainmheach-beò.

UNCERTAINTY

Walking across the beach,
my eyes on my destination;
not knowing if the tide
is turning
setting me walking
on quicksand.

Valerie Gillies

IN MEMORY OF IVOR GURNEY

Ivor Gurney, poet. Gassed near Passchendaele.
A patient at Bangour War Hospital, Autumn 1917.
Died, London asylum, 1937. Complete poems
published, 1954.

It's always that spooky light in November,
the winter lightlessness. He liked that too,
Ivor, an inmate here, a trench-companion.

The hospital had its own station then.
Three short blasts on the steam hooter to say
the ambulance train was arriving in darkness.

Stretcher-bearers at the shed with lamps
lit. Alerted by telegram, *300 tonight*.
Some sitting, some lying prone, fever cases,

or with gassing and shellshock. Like Ivor.
Tents for the thousands of angry amputees.
Tree-stumps in the leaf-litter woods,

plane and lathe in the peg-leg workshop,
a basket wheelchair with a headlamp. Now
it's tossed out on the skip. Under floorboards

lie a stack of glass negatives, medical photos
of head injuries, warriors' faces blown away.
Birch trees erupt through the station platform.

Rody Gorman

BRISEADH-LATHA

Luaisg mi às mo chadal
Nam aonar aig briseadh-latha
Nuair a dh' fhairich mi bhuam do cheum
A' dlùthachadh ris an taigh;

Smaoinich thusa! na bh' agam
De mhealladh 's de bhriseadh-dùil
Nuair nach d' fhuair mi air mo bheulaibh
Ach caora,
Aon chaora leatha fhèin ri mèilich
Gu truagh anns an sgarthanaich.

DAWN CHORUS

I awoke early with a start,
early, on my own at that
when I heard your footstep
approaching the house;

For crying out loud!
talk about a dizzie
when all I found was a sheep
a pathetic little sheep all alone
bleating in the dawn.

Yvonne Gray

SEPTEMBER

From time to time we hear it call
from high in the mountain,
tin-clank of ruptured cowbell
carrying down from a distant saeter.

On the fjord below, the pilot, gliding westwards,
slits smooth skin of water. We linger on
in the evening sunlight, watching,
speaking softly. I trace
the hairline crack on thin glass
as we sip the last red wine.

In the glow of burnished orchards the byre
stands empty, ox-blood paint darkening
as shadows slice down mountain walls.
The blue ice door is open.

Robert Green

UNTITLED

We need food before we go out drinking. You bring a casserole dish half filled with soup into the living room, onto the table. You pick off bits of bread and drop them in, cover them and scoop them out. I scoop and lean forward, watching for drips, and if we were dogs and this was spaghetti, if Disney did gay guys in Glasgow with more money for drink than sense, this would be romantic. But they don't and it's just friends.

'what time are you wanting to head?'
'anytime you're ready.'

I'm a fantasy. Turning up in your room at the end of the night, drunk and laughing, to strip to my boxers and get in bed beside you. You're only wearing a t-shirt and ask if you should take it off.

'yes.'

Half sleeping with drink and the cold, as I get ready to leave, I'm sure you're watching me.

Ian Hunter

GREY BABY

Just a nick the midwife says
the blade and the blood moving
everything up a gear
the sliver of scalp and dark hair widens
as the head emerges and you
stand ready, scissors in your hand,
names on your lips,
like some ship-launching ceremony
but the champagne goes quickly flat
with the sight of the cord around the
baby's neck
to heighten the drama the monitor
now refuses to show any heartbeat
and you can't seem to get the words
oh fuck oh fuck oh fuck
out of your head
as you stand rigid, until elbowed
aside by the other midwife
naming and cutting forgotten now
your sweaty hand holding your wife
back from the edge of exhaustion
and the baby appears
a boy, grey, lifeless
like some sort of glistening frog
waiting for dissection
arms and legs stretched out, frozen
the shock of life too great
we'll just clean out his tubes
the midwife says as they take
away your son
and your wife's hand opens
hours of effort and drugs take
their toll

she slips away, leaving you
not quite alone, but still the loneliest
you have ever felt
while you stand, shuffling,
after seven hours,
desperate for a pee,
just desperate

Linda Jackson

GOOD LICKS AREN'T EVERYTHING

He was gorgeous; all her pals thought so. The only thing was his tongue, it was like a budgie's in shape – perfectly round. However this was more like a python's in size, probing and poking about her face. She was just reaching the vomiting stage when her father remembered to rattle the living room window. I'll have to go, my dad goes crazy.

Sticky and smudged with whitish slabbers, she made for the bathroom; boke, aagh revolting – never again.

Downstairs the television rattled away as her father asked, *Was the timing ok there Daughter?*

Winnie knew she had asked him to call her in but now she felt kind of embarrassed. God knows what her dad thought it was all about – certainly not the lizarding white slabbers, that's for sure.

She said her night nights and headed up to her room.

It was much later when she got up from her bed and opened the wardrobe. It was like this sometimes when sleep wouldn't come. She prolonged her little ceremonies.

In the light of the lamp post shining from outside, she slowly opened the tin. Inside everything was as it should be:

> A nest of cotton wool soaked in perfume, a poem from the Romeo, an indistinct old photo, two stones and a name on a carefully cut piece of paper.

She stared inside savouring all the love she felt, she bowed her head slowly into the casket of her dreaming.

It was a long time before she felt the start of a stiff neck creak bent as she was under the top bunk bed. She closed the butterscotch tin quickly and replaced it under the scarves on her wardrobe shelf.

As she turned, a face looked out at her from the wavering old mirror on the back of the door.

Slowly she began to lick the girl in the glass; she kissed her with open eyes and, finally locking them closed, began to lift the edge of her skirt. Round and round her head twisted passionately, her legs wrapped themselves tightly – pulling her closer until finally one of the eyes opened and – caught her...

caught her licking glass.

She pulled her fingers free and began to pray

> I must die
> I don't know where
> I don't know when
> I don't know how
> But if I die in mortal sin
> I am lost forever.

Fuck's sake, that's really terrifying, her granny was a bad old bastard teaching her that – especially with her kissing mirrors and poking around squelchy bits and thinking the way she did about white sticky patches on her Summer dress.

She knew she'd see him again soon. He'd stand in the club with his friends and the air would sharpen as Marie whispers, he's here. Walking past her friends with him, she felt great really. The road home took ages and he told her all about his band and the music he liked and he told her about his brother Eddie and she thought *he's* gorgeous.

But it would soon be time for the lamp post, the stories would finish. How far tonight with the lizard?

Paula Jennings

GRETEL

Were the warnings encoded in frog-croak

or in the urgent chirrup of a bird?
She arrived so young at the gingerbread house,
didn't hear them,
knocked at the chocolate door,
tore at the marzipan lintel,
eager and greedy.

She forgot she was looking for home.
What was it anyway? Just bread and parents,
nothing she can use now, and besides,
they lied about the witch,
there's no hook-nosed warty evil here.

He brings her magic in a needle,
fairytale stuff,
tells her she is sugar and honey,
and she believes him, doesn't feel
the toffee walls begin to shake and sweat,
her sweet shelter caving in.

Years pass, and I follow the trail
of breadcrumbs back to the ruined door.
The cage is still there.
Sunshine filters through the bars,
pools amber on my sister's bones.

I gather boughs of pine and juniper,
heap them on the ground,
arrange the bones like petals
round the quiet skull,
tibia and fibula, the slender curves of ribs;
a white flower on a bed of dark needles.

The smoke is a straight road upward
through the waiting air;
we travel it together,
my sister's spirit and my song.
I'm singing our footsteps on the long path,
I'm singing us home.

Helen Lamb

Fom: *Thirteen Spells*

SPELL OF THE BRIDGE

Hold the wish on your tongue
as you cross
what the bridge cannot hear
cannot fall

For the river would carry
your hopes to the sea
to the net of a stranger
to the silt bed of dreams

Hold the wish on your tongue
as you cross
and on the far side
let the wish go first

Euan McCulloch

THE BULLET SPED

trigger trigger trig the bullet sped oh so it sped
the boy was dead like the girl she was a beauty just so
in the street where the cars were violent as acid
wastepaper and cigarette packets sat in the gutter
untidy while the dust was sore like sand in the eye
and the bird in the tree sang
a dipshit saxophone player in the city
I was sad as hell because of the world
girls children and men
while the sirens were a keening

Murdo Stal MacDonald

EADAR ÀIRD A' MHÀSAIR IS OSTAIG

A' Chiad Latha
Craobh às deaghaidh craoibh
Air a cnòdach
Le geansaidh còinneach crotail.

An Dàrna Latha
Creamh fiathaich gham ithe
Gach madainn gu bracaist
Conas gham ithe gach tràth.

An Treas Latha
Bogha-frois' am beul a' ghlinne
Ri pògadh na mara,
'S beul fosgailt' na Linne.

An Ceathramh Latha
Cur is dlùth na coille
Air fhighe nam fhèithean
Air rathad Liosa Shlèite.

An Còigeamh Latha
Truimead na culma
Ri doth air na Garbh Chrìochan
Man leanabh air màthair.

An Siathamh Latha
Mèilich nan uan
Man seisd ri gach duan
'S a' chuthag ri togail an fhuinn.

An Seachdamh Latha
A' leigeil na mo shìneadh
Air brat-ùrlair na coille
Bròg-na-cuthaig gham thoinneamh.

An t-Ochdamh Latha
Seilleanan nam màl
'S ri leughadh na tìde,
Ri tional am bidhe gun dàil.

An Naoidheamh Latha
Neo-ar-thaing nach robh mi aoibhneach
Led sgeirean cho coibhneil
A' moladh an latha dhomh.

An Deicheamh Latha
Lòin-dhubha is smeòraich
A' cumail a' chàirdeis
Ann an càil an latha.

BETWEEN ARDVASAR AND OSTAIG

The First Day
Tree after tree
Clothed
In mossy chenille.

The Second Day
Eaten by wild garlic
For breakfast daily,
Each mealtime, I am, by gorse.

The Third Day
Rainbow touches glen
Kisses ocean
And Sound's soft lips.

The Fourth Day
Wooded warp and weft
Knitted with my veins
In the Garden of Sleat.

The Fifth Day
Heavy mists
Cling to mainland peaks
Like a child.

The Sixth Day
Lambs bleat
The chorus of the song
The cuckoo sings in tune.

The Seventh Day
Lying down to rest
On bluebell woodland carpet
Twisting, twisting.

The Eighth Day
A busy bee-body
A-weather-forecasting
A-food-collecting.

The Ninth Day
Surprised by joy
As your kind skerries
Bid me good morning.

The Tenth Day
Blackbirds and thrushes
Cèilidh-ing
In the twilight.

James McGonigal

from: *Poems Written for Translation into an Abandoned Language*

MAKING LIGHT OF IT

My daughter phones from Spain
at the start of the eclipse
insisting that it has grown darker
five minutes earlier than up here –
ola, the black mouth of the moon
swallowing the sun's gold egg
with pitiless lipsmacking gusto.

She was surprised that I sounded
so noncommital – me an aficionado
of archetype lenses. Claire, it's partly
the other sight of our kind which catches
demons in shadows every day and angels
on a fairly regular basis returning
from the shop with their gold string bags

weightless with oatmeal, cheese and potatoes.
And partly that up here we are used to
living benighted, abandoned by sunbeams,
miasmatic, occluded, the auburn of youth
turning grey as your noon sky in Fuente today.

TOWARDS THE FIRE

No matter how deeply the darkness offends you
it will never say sorry.

These nights we know it is a flame we lack
and smoke-tanned skin

with ash in every whorl and pore.
Smoke rises

but the cone of fuel is hugging heat
close to its chest

while seawinds tie the reek from our chimney
into a sailor's lucky knot

and cast it far out on the tides of heaven
to fetch stars in

to the sharp hooks of flame in this hearth.

Rob Mackenzie

LAST DANCE

Mac dances tap on
a rag of squashed chips.

The party's over, the pubs
shut. He shovels down
a deep-fried pizza
at half-eleven after
seven hours' drinking.
Vomits a pic'n'mix on
the square's concrete slabs.
Statues smeared with pigeon
shit are the only ones
who don't turn away.

Recalls the night he drank
with sweet death in the driving
seat of a stolen wreck;
crashed out rat-arsed,
haggis parked between his
teeth, Y-fronts steered
round his ears. Life on
the highway, fast cars,
a busload of cheap booze,
an attitude to match.

He dodges the pre-clubbing
crowd's post-ironic
retrospection. Searches
a way home, an alley
to take him somewhere.
Walks straight as a Roman
road, cracks snapping at
his ankles. Trips off the
world's edge, trapped in
the lights of a speeding taxi.

A flap of brown paper
waves beneath the wheel.

Anne MacLeod

LEAVING CAPE BRETON FOR THE BLACK ISLE; 1999
leaving, I have come to know
the gold, the russet green, the yellow
of my black not-island

not black ever, blonde from June
through January, till the black earth
tilled, sprouts winter wheat
                              too green, too soon
defying leaves, dried coins
on burning ground
                    (harvest long gone
          fields adrift)

leaving, I have learned the golden tune
your island's measure

beannachd leibh

Ellen McNair

RAMPOLINI & FRAME

Zoe wriggles her backside on the bidet's cold edge, watches Stella stuff sachets into her pockets.

On the other side of the door is a middle-aged man with a hard-on.

Zoe's tired of it all. 'Can't I just watch the telly?' she whines. 'I'll keep the sound down.'

Stella sniffs a wrapped wafer of soap. 'And leave me to do all the work? No fucking way.'

They go through to the room stuffed with double-bed, television, mini-bar, trouser-press. The man – what was his name again? Dougie? Archie? – sits against the headboard, tightening his stomach muscles.

Zoe squeezes through the gap between the bed and the TV, crawls along the floor to the mini-bar. She likes mini-bars. They remind her of the toys she always wanted when she was wee; a pretend kitchen, with fridge, cooker, ironing-board and washing-machine. She pours two vodka and cokes, drops a crushed tranquilliser in one, and passes them over her head to Stella.

Zoe doesn't like the men Stella chooses. She couldn't do what they do if she did.

She couldn't do it to the guys she sees during the day; the ones going up and down the hill, to and from the art school. Sometimes, if it's nice, she goes down for a closer look. It's not that she fancies them: it's much more than that. They're nothing like any guy she's ever known; nothing like her da or her brothers or the boys at school. It fascinates her that they go about with girls; girls who don't seem to be their girlfriends. One or two have even said hello when she's been hanging about outside the art school café.

No matter how many times she sees it, Zoe thinks there's nothing more disgusting than the sight of a hairy arse going up and down.

'Oh, oh, oh,' goes Stella.

'Ah, ah, ah,' goes the man.

Zoe flicks listlessly across the channels. She can hear the sex, the wet clicks and plops. She can smell it, which is worse than hearing and seeing put together.

'Wait,' goes Stella, with faked breathlessness.

'What for?' goes the man.

Zoe reaches into her bag and chucks a johnnie over her head. There's a paper tear, a snap of rubber.

Zoe wonders if it's true what Stella says, that guys who go to art school are poofs.

Stella hates poofs; says they hate girls even more than normal guys. She's forever slagging off the couple who live on the close, down on the ground floor. 'I've seen them holding hands,' she says, poking two fingers in her mouth.

Zoe pretends to agree, but she secretly likes the two men. They've got brass plates on their storm doors, saying *Rampolini* and *Frame*. She pondered their identity for ages and decided that the tall dark-haired one must be the Italian, and the other, the small skinny one with the cropped blond hair, must be Frame.

When the moans die away, when Stella climbs off and goes to the bathroom, Zoe stands up. The man looks injured. He's panting, a deep crease between his eyebrows. Zoe stands at the side of the bed looking down on him. Just the once, just this time, why can't he conk out before she has to do it? The man pats the bed.

Zoe thinks about the art school boys when he's doing it to her; hardly notices when he goes *aaaaaaahhhhhh* like he's been stabbed in the back.

Rampolini and Frame go out together most nights. If Stella's pissed, and she usually is, Zoe pulls on a jacket and follows them into town. They always go to the same bar down by the Clyde. Usually it's too cold to hang about so Zoe sits in the bus station café till they chuck her out for not buying anything.

One night, Frame leaves the bar by himself and heads back into the centre of town. Zoe follows at a distance, tracking him up to Sauchiehall Street and then along Woodlands Road, where he turns into the park.

Zoe goes through the iron gates, head swivelling like a bottle top. She sees a man crossing the grass but it isn't Frame. She starts walking back to the gates. Why would he want to talk to her anyway? Why would he want to talk to a fat boring ugly girl like her? She looks over her shoulder. The man joins the footpath, but he veers off before he gets to her, stepping through a gap in a tall hedge. Another man comes through the gap from the opposite direction.

She thinks it must be a short-cut.

Zoe wipes herself with damp toilet paper. Her fingers smell of rubber. She stands in front of the mirror, rearranging her clothes. Her jeans feel tight, the right thigh more than the left. In the mirror, she can see the man, lying there totally out of it. Beside him on the bed, an open wallet.

She goes through to the room. 'How much?' she says, wearily.

Stella is on her knees, taking what's left of the mini-bar. 'Fifty each, plus those.' She nods at cufflinks, watch, pen.

Everything is frozen. It feels like she's walking through a photograph. She can see figures, still as sculptures, leaning against the trees. Out of the corner of her eye, something moves. Her arm is taken and she is led back through the gap in the hedge.

It's Frame, only it turns out he isn't Frame, he's Rampolini, even though he looks nothing like an Italian. 'What the hell are you doing here?' he hisses.

'I don't know,' she says, feeling like she's going to cry. 'I only wanted to say hello.'

His face softens. 'For God's sake, don't you know what this place is?'

She shakes her head, though she's beginning to understand.

Zoe sits at the window, looking up at the inky sky. She's thinking about the men in the park, trying to imagine what it is they get up to. Below, on the street, she sees Rampolini duck into the close. He goes to the park most nights, after dark.

She stands up and pulls on her jacket.

Stella struggles drunkenly onto her elbows. 'Where the fuck're you going?'

'Shops.'

'Wha for?'

'Crisps and ginger.'

Stella sneers. 'Don't you think you're fucking fat enough?'

Zoe taps lightly on the etched glass, notices that the plate saying Frame has gone.

The door opens immediately. Rampolini stands there, in white jeans and T-shirt, face dropping because it isn't who he expects, or wants it to be. 'Oh, hi.'

Zoe points to the four screw-holes in the wood. 'What happened?'

'Oh, that,' he says, dismissively.

'He's gone?'

Rampolini covers his face. His shoulders do a sad little dance.

Zoe puts her hand on his bare arm. She feels the smooth warm skin, the underlying muscle, all taut and twisted. He doesn't shrug her off like she expects, so she strokes the arm, slowly from shoulder to elbow. He leans into her and her arm finds its way around his narrow back. He smells fresh, lemony.

'Look at us standing here like two silly women,' he says, all muffled against her jacket.

Zoe removes her arm.

'Life goes on,' he says, straightening up.

Zoe thinks about Stella. In Stella's world, life never goes on. Everything's at a standstill; stuck in an endless, vicious rut.

'Are you going to stand there like that all night?' he says amiably, holding open the door.

Zoe climbs slowly to the top floor. The light is on in the hall, the naked bulb dangling like a luminous hand-grenade. She listens keenly. Gas hisses, the fire twangs. She pushes the living-room door, her breathing suspended. Everything's as it should be, apart from a wee mound of vomit on the rug.

Stella's bed is ruffled up but it's empty and cold.

Zoe opens the door to her own bedroom. The curtains are parted, the room hazy with dun light. Stella's on the bed, clutching the pillow like she's hanging off a cliff-edge. There's a smell of sick, tinged with alcohol. Zoe sits on the bed, feels Stella's body roll against her. There's a bump on her forehead that's already bruising, a crustiness around the mouth.

Stella opens her eyes. 'I thought you were never coming back,' she murmurs.

'I wouldn't have that cow anywhere near me,' says Rampolini, laying a chequered cloth over a table by the window.

'She looks after me,' Zoe says. 'If it wasn't for her I wouldn't have anywhere to live.'

Rampolini snorts. 'You can do better than her, trust me.' He sets out cups and saucers, side plates and napkins. 'Why don't you get a place of your own?'

'How?' she says. 'I haven't got any money.'

Rampolini opens a box of cakes and positions them on the table. 'You could get a job,' he says. 'A *proper* job, I mean.' He points at the cakes. 'Help yourself.'

Zoe picks a chocolate eclair and bites into it. It melts like Holy Communion against the roof of her mouth. She looks around the flat: it's all so neat, so pretty, so nice.

Rampolini pours pale tea through a strainer. 'So?' he says. 'Are you going to get off your butt and do something with your life?'

Zoe sips the delicate, scented tea. It seems to her like a door is opening, a door she knew was there but one she thought would never open for her.

Iain S. Mac a' Phearsain

AM FÒN

am fòn na thosd
gaoth a-muigh
gèile a-staigh

THE PHONE

the phone silent
a wind without
a gale within

AINGEAL NA DÙBHLACHD

a leithid dùbhlachd
chan fhaca mi

nas miosa na bhith a' dol fodha
a-muigh ann am meadhan Loch a' Mhathain Mhòir
air Oidhche Challainn air choreigin
's na rionnagan dheth

nas fhaide na rathad na h-òigridh
a' teàrnadh nam bliadhnaichean
eadar anail nad uchd
's sgìths nad phòig

nas dùinte
na bìoball bodaich
nach maireann

's mi grunnachadh san t-sneachda
ri guidheachan a-mach
a' dèanamh aingeal le mo mhùin
tuill ann an anart geamhraidh

DECEMBER ANGEL

i've never seen
such a december

worse than going under
out in the middle of Great Bear Lake
some new year's eve or other
and the stars put out

longer than the road of youth
winding down the years
between your breathlessness
and your blasé kiss

more shut
than a dead old
bodach's bible

i wading in the snow
cursing out loud
making angels with my piss
holes in winter's shroud

TIODHLACADH BAILE IS CLACHAN FUAR

gabhaidh e thairis os ar cionn mar a' ghaoth
thuirt am ministear ris an uaigh
oir 's e seo ar crìoch uile
ged nach tàinig a dheireadh orra fhathast

's fir a' bhaile mun cuairt air
a' freagairt gairm a' bhàis
gus Seonaidh 'An Alasdair
a leigeil sìos
gu grunnd na sìorraidheachd
far nach eil na h-uibhir ann co-dhiù

's an clachan rag reòidhte
a' fàgail cladh na sgìre
a' teàrnadh a' bhruthaich anns a' ghaoith

cha robh e cho fada an-diugh

TOWNSHIP FUNERAL AND COLD STONES

it shall pass over us like the wind
said the minister to the grave
for this is all our end
though they hadn't heard the end of it yet

and the men of the village round about him
answering the call of death
to lower Johnny John Sandy
down
to the arse-end of eternity
where there's not that much anyhow

and their nuts frozen stiff
leaving the parish cemetery
winding downhill in the wind

he wasn't so long today

John Maley

MOTHERSHIP

Joan took another drag of her cigarette and then stubbed it out on her mother's face. Her mother was silent for a few moments – delayed reaction – then let out a yell. Then she fell silent again. Joan looked down at the frail, bony body of her mother adrift on the big double bed. The dishevelled blankets. Her mother's beautiful silver hair. Her puzzled, child-like expression.

She ran into the lobby and stood, gasping suddenly for air, her back arched against the wall. It wasn't so much what she had done as the ease with which she had done it. Her mother stayed silent now.

The light was on in the bathroom. Through the frosted glass window of the door a yellowish light glowed. Joan could smell the shite from the toilet. The mess her mother made. She couldn't bear to clean it tonight but couldn't bear to leave it till morning. Her mother was an artist in that toilet and her palate was the seven colours of shite. Joan had tried going into the toilet with her mother but it had only led to more grief than it was worth. She had decided to giver her mother a free rein and then go in later with her rubber gloves and disinfectant, her mood fluctuating between a quiet professionalism and a dignified revulsion.

Sometimes Joan would watch her mother from the lobby. Through the window she'd see her mother, framed in the square of yellow light, the frosted glass. The shadow of her mother, the noises she made, the murmurings and mutterings, the spill of light down the darkened lobby. It made her think of spaceships. A spaceship that had landed at the bottom of her lobby. And inside, an alien. An extra-terrestrial. A skinny angular figure babbling a strange language. An old woman lost in time and space.

The first time her mother looked at her, lost and confused, without recognition, seemed an eternity ago. Joan had her suspicions for a while before that, but there was something chilling about that look, that day, as her mother fumbled for her keys and looked up and down, fumbling and frowning. Was she terrified? Was this the last thing they had shared? Maybe there was no turning point. No particular moment. But now. Now her mother was gone and there instead was an alien, a bodysnatcher, with her weird memories, her wild madness.

The smell of shite from her mother's spaceship was beginning to get to Joan. Soon she would have to do something. Still
no sound from her mother. Would she be feeling the burn on
her face? Joan thought of going to the medicine cabinet for
some Germolene. Her mother swore by Germolene. But the
medicine cabinet was really the bathroom cabinet and the
bathroom cabinet was in the bathroom and the bathroom was
also the toilet and the toilet smelled of shite. Why the delay?
Why delay the inevitable? Why did her mother wait to yell?
Had she refused to recognise her pain?

Joan had accommodated these things into her life. Mad
mothers, spaceships, rubber gloves, disinfectant, down on her
knees scrubbing the linoleum. She had dressed and undressed
her mother like a careful little girl her favourite doll. She had
taken to translating for her mother. Decoding her raving, her
havering, into something semi-coherent, whether it be a banal
request for practical assistance, or some beautiful or terrible
memory that had fought its way through the fuddle to haunt
them both. One day she had been havering about crisps and
crumbs on your skirt and Joan remembered when she was a wee
lassie just started primary school her mother used to meet her at
the bottle-green school railings and pass through crisps – or a
fruit scone she had baked – or some sweeties, at playtime. At
first the memory of that made Joan smile but then she thought
of an ulterior motive for her mother's attentiveness. That with
her starting school her mother would have been lonely those
mornings. Her older brother Charlie had started school a few
years before. So there was her mother, a widow at thirty-five,
reaching to her wee lassie through the school railings. Worried
her lassie would be walking around with crumbs on her skirt.
Doing that fussy rubbing thing with slabbery fingers. Just a wee
stain there, hen. Mind you keep yourself tidy.

Put her in a home. Charlie was such a selfish bastard she
could have strangled him. In fact she would almost certainly
have throttled him if he had said that in her presence. But he
was on the phone from London, playing the concerned son.
Joan had a fair idea what these old folks' homes were like. The
smells of pish and boiled cabbage, the screams of old women
being scalded in baths of boiling water by glaikit sixteen year
olds. The sly flick of a wet towel knocking some old guy's glass
eye out. Rows of mouths muttering to themselves, each with

the wrong false teeth in. Naw, Charlie. This is her home.
Anyway it's no your problem. I'm the one doing the fetching
and carrying.

A sudden paranoia gripped her. What if Charlie made a
surprise visit? What if he noticed a burn mark on mammy's
face and asked in all innocence had she burned herself? Aye,
she'd say. No elaborations. That's how liars get caught.
Embellishments. Talking themselves into trouble. She could
never lie to Charlie. He was such an overbearing big bastard.
Still playing the surrogate father. Some people never move on.
Some people don't move an inch. She could almost laugh at
herself now, frozen against the lobby wall. Unable to reach the
bathroom or go back into her mother's room. Stuck in a kind
of limbo in the lobby.

A sudden thought came to her. A kind of detour. There was
some gin and tonic water in the cabinet in the living room. If
she was to sit with a drink to steady herself. Then she could
face her mother again, and scrub the toilet – and her conscience
– clean as a whistle before crashing out. A wee gin and tonic.
Close her eyes for a minute. Take some deep breaths.

She manoeuvred herself into the living room. That was the
only word for it, manoeuvred. Like a tank rumbling over
potential landmines in a war zone. There were times she was so
grateful for quiet that even so much as a sigh from her mother
seemed like a grenade going off. Then it was into the cabinet
and out with the gin and the tonic. She pulled out a glass. It
looked a bit manky but rather than have to go to the kitchen
and wash it she just gave it a rub with the hem of her blouse.
Clarty cow, she said to herself, before taking that first tentative
sip. It was always better to the taste when you poured it yourself. Joan couldn't understand all this measures baloney you got
in pubs. Why couldn't you just say when?

The living room clock's tick-tock started to get louder and
louder. Or maybe the house was simply getting quieter and
quieter. Her mother had once remarked that 'that clock's
worth money, hen'. Aye mammy, thought Joan. So is an empty
ginger bottle if you take it back to the shops. Now her mother couldn't tell the time. That wasn't actually true. It wasn't
that she didn't know how to read the clock. It was just that it
didn't mean anything to her. If she got up during the night then
that was morning to her. She had no firm grasp on past, present or future. She spent half her life in her nightdress. But for

now she was quiet and the clock ticked on and on, ticking out time, a language totally foreign now.

You're havering, lassie, she'd say. If that wasn't putting the tin lid on it what was? There was her mammy gadding about without her false teeth in, a skidmark on her nightdress, blethering away like a lunatic. But judge folk by the company they keep. It was contagious. Like the way people goo-goo and ga-ga over babies on the bus. You slipped into the lingo. When in Rome etcetera. All she could do was keep her as clean as she could and as calm as she could. Which was easier said than done. It was a funny kind of role reversal. To see your mammy turning into your wean. A wean that needed a right good skelpin'. But she had never hurt her mother like that. Not till tonight. She couldn't think about it. She wouldn't think about it. She'd draw a discreet veil over the whole thing. Que Sera Sera. That's what her mother would sing to her when she was wee. God, she had a screw loose even then. Careering around the kitchen, her voice flat as a big pancake, whatever will be will be. What her mother lacked in talent, she made up for in enthusiasm. Vivacity filled the vacuum.

She should phone Charlie. But that was no good. He'd haver about finding a nursing home and how busy he was and say he'd phone her in the morning. Then he wouldn't phone. There was the danger she'd confess over the phone and he'd get her locked up as well. She'd end up with her name in the papers. The spooky spinster who used her mammy's sonsie face as an ashtray. The judge ordered her to be detained without limit of time – and to give up smoking. Naw. Silence was golden. It was like a gold ring that encompassed Joan and her mammy. A big, gold ring with 'Wheesht' engraved on it. That had been her mother's battle-cry when Joan and Charlie were wee and getting out of hand. Wheesht! And they would fall silent and lie like wee lambs. She used wheesht on her mother when she got noisy but it was no use. She spat her own medicine back in Joan's face.

She drained the last of her gin. Doon the hatch. Another one wouldn't go amiss. Mine's a double. A Barney Rubble. Say when. Say wheesht. She poured herself a generous measure of gin and tonic. She took a slow, indulgent sip and sank further into the armchair. She could turn on the telly and see what was on. But that would disturb the peace. Maybe put on a tape, down low. One of the great composers. Gustav Mahler. Barry

Manilow. But why disturb the peace? Why breach the peace? The peace that passeth understanding. The jeely piece your mammy used to throw down from the window as the strains of Andy Stewart wafted out from behind the billowing curtains and shoogled around the back courts. These days it wasn't jeely pieces she was throwing out of the window, it was cutlery, Joan's knickers, library books. You needed a bloody crash helmet to pass that window.

Her mother's decline had divided Joan's neighbours into two major camps. There were the nosey bastards who had developed insensitivity into an art form. And then there were the sad old pals of her mammy who valiantly tried to hide their embarrassment, sadness and fear with old familiarities and reminiscences, attempting to cajole from her mother some hollow acknowledgement of old friendship which had, like so many other things, fallen by the wayside. They would respond for her, remember for her, laugh for her, shake their heads for her, passing off monologues as dialogues and tragedy as farce. All those anchors had been cast off these past couple of years and the Mothership was steaming steadily towards oblivion. There was no land ahoy.

Joan took another sip of gin and closed her eyes. Her eyes felt tired and sore. She would rest them awhile. In the darkness she could hear the clock ticking and feel the glass in her fist. She had been burned once. On the hand. She had been at the Barras with her mother and a big, brassy peroxide blonde woman had been brandishing a cigarette around as she effed and blinded at a bewildered man in her company. Joan had tried to squeeze past the blonde, holding onto her mother, but the floozy's fag had burned into the back of her hand. Joan gave a gasp at the pain. The blonde had immediately acknowledged the injury and threw her arms around Joan, smothering her with kisses. Oh the wee pet. Ah've burnt the wee pet. Joan's mother had stood woodenly in the background. Joan had burst into tears, not at the burn, but at this sudden burst of affection and warmth.

Joan finished the second G & T and went through to check on her mother. She was sitting up in bed and in the lamplight the red mark on her face was cruelly visible. She was saying something but Joan couldn't make out what it was. She sat down on the bed.

'What is it mammy?'

She listened to the sound again and again. Gradually it was becoming audible, decipherable. Burny, she was saying. As Joan took her mother in her arms she heard a small cry come from her. She looked up at her and Joan hoped to God her mother was truly lost now. She wept and buried her face in her mammy's silver hair and rocked her in her arms.

Andy Manders

SCOTTISH JOURNEY

Glasgow

only the light
for the briefest moment held beyond ourselves
catching a wetness about the eye

and the silence
willing hands built between us
in which the moment passes

till finally, like any other myth, Glasgow is
deid n done with
the weight of being *illuminated*.

The Athens of the North

the bus driver in the Blue Blanket bog reciting Dunbar
is not the democratic intellect
not in person anyway

so you invent the Cuillins
choke the mist from their throats
wringing for songs

in Wester Hailes everyone speaks gaelic
no one is poor
remarkably

life goes on.

The Highlands

kipping down
in a bothy run by sheep
(the stench something fearful)

the middle of nowhere
with wildcats and madmen on manoeuvre
and occasionally

crossing our minds
the slow, dark and crooked, pointy finger
of the thick, eerie-black air

silent outside.

some place.

The Streets of Raith

tonight there will be a man
without a country
dance on one of its beaches

The Wee Bit By The Loch On The Back Road Out Of Milton Of Cushnie

the collective unconscious
is gathering
to celebrate
its complete irrelevance
to present day Scotland

watch oot

Dundee All Over Scotland

'all over Scotland
tomorrow morning
people will be

alive
with a new sense of purpose'

I just assumed it was Orson Welles
you went shopping
you didn't even notice

the walls that were supposed to crumble

Sutherland

the last tree in Scotland
and a crow in it

two crows
and my consciousness of them

a parliament and everything
much as it should be

while the woman like a wall who waits
by the house of her birth to leave

goes alone
they haul themselves sky-wards

Patrick Sellar is nowhere to be seen
this is 1999

Aberdein

like granite and the light
skelping off it

the way the wave
pronounces the word brine

The Proper Bits Of Fife

imagining keepie-ups forever Hampdened in his head
the wee fellow without the ball
and the last of the light

jink their way across the red ash
dark and defenders trailing

but for the glass and shit
and the not being home an hour ago

his pitch is infinite

Consolations of Scotland

in this wet land
of forever small mountains

the likelihood

of step
        step
            stepping

across the sweet blue distance
of their tops

is all the greater

Donald S. Murray

OLD TEACHER

That teacher was a lighthouse on the headland.
Granite built on gneiss,
she did not stir
in doubt or storm
but weathered every breaking wave
with indifference to its force.

A landmark marked on all our charts,
that foghorn voice
boomed psalm and catechism;
her means of navigating
life's mists and hazards
relayed to small vessels harboured in that room.

Her belt a signal sent out
in distress and desperation;
each blow a beam
flicking left and right
flashed to those fixed on a hell-bound course
for all the warnings of her light.

Liz Niven

TOURISTS AT AUSCHWITZ

We'd been telt
nae birds wid sing.

True it wis bit tall trees
shrooded brick wark camps.

Row upon row, they stretcht,
far as the greetin een cuid see.

Hidden fae view,
gas chaumers lay buriet,
unner foondations crummlt,
as butcher builders fleed.

A million an a hauf stanes pave
memorials in monie tungs.
A brick fir ilka deid sowel.
Vyces are low, few picters taen.

Nearhaun, a watter-fillt hollow,
algae covert, still hauds human ash.
A haun-wringin guide tells us mair.
Wirds hing heavy.

Intae sic silence,
a green puddock lowps a perfit bow,
oan the staignant loch.

Tom Pow

SIMON IN THE VEGETABLE PATCH
For Erin

At the end of rows of runner beans –
perfect, proud, erect – your peas,
equally perfect and sweet as I remember –

a taste in tact from childhood –
lie in a tangle of their own devising.
With a bundle of canes like pick up sticks,

a ball of twine, a knife as red
as a rooster's comb whose blade
winks in the sun, you spend an afternoon

half-hour, no real notion
what you're doing, only what you want
to achieve – to bring those peas to order!

You think in planes, in angles,
in zigs and zags: a stage set for peas
to shine like blades, to lift themselves

onto open palms. Somehow it's disaster.
But at least it's half an hour
when not much else is happening.

Your daughter tops a white cap
with sunshine, her eyes the centre
of all that is; a picture that spirals

beyond her mother, her mother's friends,
the busy hens, the pony that stands,
head bowed in private penance;

out yet to green maps of alder and ash
that ripple with health till the blue sky
clips them. But at last, hey ho,

a solution. Your blade rides
through knotted twine; you amass
an airy pile of branches. *Something*

more informal, you say. Too late!
The company calls on you – a walk
to the grey, roiling sea. And sweetly

you accept, though there'll be nothing to show
for this half hour of all your labours –
as there's nothing to show

for half an hour when your daughter
sat in the sun and smiled and laughed
at her mother, her mother's friends,

the busy hens, the penitent pony,
and the ash, the alder, the rows
of runner beans and peas where her father

worked carefully, without care,
puzzling over a tiny piece of green chaos
while there was order everywhere.

Wayne Price

WHERE I LIVE

It's midday, end of August, and for one last time I'm riding the Amtrak north out of New England. I've got a letter I need to write, things that have to be said, and I'm thinking I'd have more chance if the guy two seats back would just shut up a while and let me think straight, let me hear what I'm trying to say. He wandered into the carriage an hour ago; young, thin, red-headed with a scrap of beard, dressed loose and carrying an army stores pack like he should be wandering some trail, not riding a commuter line. He found the seat where the little girl was sleeping and joined her. When she woke he started talking in his low, sleepy monotone, and hasn't stopped since.

Where I live, he's saying now, we get trains maybe once, maybe twice a week. Way up north, that's the way it is. It's pretty lonesome. But pretty peaceful, too. He pauses. I guess it's both.

The girl must be about eleven or twelve. I took a good long look at her sleeping when I boarded. Other than us, the carriage was clear. Long, straight blond hair; cool, pale doll's face; doll's hands. So still, you'd doubt there was breath in her body, let alone a baggage of words.

I don't think I'd like that, she says now.

No, he says. I guess you might not. You like the country, though?

Mmm, she hums, like she doesn't want to say.

You don't like the country?

No, she laughs, embarrassed.

I love the country. I couldn't live anywhere but the country. You really don't like the country?

No, she says again, sounding a little discomforted now, almost the way she sounded when she first woke to find him next to her. I don't like bugs and stuff, she apologises.

Oh I get it now, he says, lightening up, winning her back. You're right not to like the bugs, he says. He whistles a single trailing note. Where I live, the bugs sometimes, they can eat you alive.

I'll bet, she agrees, happier again. I know what that's like from camp and stuff. When I was a kid.

You know, you'll probably think this is kind of gross, he goes on, but where I live, in the summer, we don't use deodorant

or anything. I mean we wash and all. But nobody wears deodorant because it draws the bugs. But I don't know – you probably
think that's gross. Even if you were at camp you'd think, *that's
gross*. You'll probably tell me that's gross, right?

She says something but for once it's too quiet for me to hear.

The worst ones are called blackfly, he says.

There's a long silence then. Maybe a minute or more. Then
there's some sort of rummaging and I remember the canvas kit-
bag he carried with him. I'm wondering what he's looking for.
See that? he says, and she lets out a giggle. Hey, he says, you
know how I'm a red-head? Well red-heads are supposed to have
something called a recessive gene. You know what genes are?

Uh huh. We studied those.

Well you know how with dogs you get, like, leader dogs
and pack dogs? Well a recessive gene means you're a pack dog.
But me, I'm kind of a leader dog. So I figure I'm, like, a mutant
or something. It's like I'm the exception that proves the rule.
You ever heard that phrase?

She asks him if he has a dog.

No, he says. Where I live is good country to keep a dog, but
I don't. Hey, he says, you know that joke, the one that goes 'it's
in your jeans?'

No, she says, and he doesn't take it further.

There's quiet again then and through the window I watch
the hot late summer sun bearing down on Vermont. I put pen
to paper but instead of writing find myself making the outline
of a nude, reclining, slender limbs wide open. I block it off, fill
the square with ink, turn back to the sun and woods. The harder I look, the more I seem to see pathways winding through the
trees though I know it's a trick of the light.

Just look at all those leaves, all ready to turn, I hear him
say, and for a second I'm startled as if it's my shoulder he's suddenly leaning at, my ear his lips are near brushing.

I stare at my hands, the smudged fingers, wet palms.

I love the fall, she replies, her own voice grown dreamier.
When the leaves get really pretty – that's so neat.

I thought you didn't like the country, all that outdoors stuff,
he teases, but gentler than he's picked at her before.

Well, y'know. She giggles at herself, then thinks for a time.
You don't get bugs in the fall.

No, he says, slow and almost melodic. No – most bugs die.

I imagine him nodding as he speaks, his pointed beard

dipping; I picture her smooth, upturned face.

You know all these woods are famous, he tells her. In songs and films. Old songs about Vermont.

I don't know, she says, They're nice though.

You like music?

Uh huh.

What kind?

Oh, I don't know. Lots of kinds I guess. I kind of like The Spice Girls.

He lets out a death-rattle and she giggles. Man oh man, you like The Spice Girls? Really?

Yeah. Well kind of.

You like those tiny little skirts they wear though? Those tiny little dresses?

She hesitates. I don't know, she says, confused.

You wouldn't wear anything like that though?

I don't know. Well, I guess not.

You like them though? I mean the band. The Spice Girls.

Yeah, she says. And The Smashing Pumpkins.

Smashing Pumpkins? Okay. Cool.

She laughs again, shyly.

You like all these woods though?

Uh huh. I like these kinds of trees. They're not like, big dark winter trees.

You mean like pines and firs and stuff, right?

Yeah. The kind you get on mountains, in snow and all.

Yeah, he muses. Where I live, it's like this.

It must be nice, in the fall.

Oh yeah. You should see the fall up there. You know, you should just miss your stop and get off with me where I'm going and see it all for yourself for a couple of days. You could do that.

I don't think so. She laughs. But she's not uncomfortable anymore.

Well, I was just kidding. Where I live, I kid people all the time.

She doesn't answer and I realise I've started drawing again.

I'm kind of known for it, he says.

I close my eyes, shift away from the window where I've been leaning. And maybe the sudden movement reminds him I'm there in front of them, because he says nothing for a long while after that, even when she says something about a deer feeding at the tree-line.

After a time I open my eyes and crane across so I can see clear down the aisle. We're almost at the tail of the long train and the far carriages beyond, where he came from, look as deserted as our own. I consider moving on into one of the last cars, but something keeps me sitting there with them, feeling the same rocks and bumps, waiting. I finish another nude, the same girl but standing this time, lewdly, and again box it, then score it all black.

I sleep for a while, wake at a small station where no-one seems to get off or on. The sun's lower now, flooding in through the glass but with a warmer, yellowish glow. Behind me, they're speaking softly, as if it's already night. I know now the words I have to write won't come, not today, and not ever. I look at the lines I've written, sign them, though God knows they can't make much sense, and fold the sheet closed. The nudes are still there, in their ink coffins.

It takes a while longer, but I know it's going to come; and the truth be told, I'm happy to see him finally wander on back with her, into the empty carriages.

Sheila Puri

COLD PAKORA

The touch of the soft cotton salvaar kameez brought a strange mixture and discomfort and pleasure. When she had first worn it to the shops Ranjit had felt invisible. No one had looked at her. People who usually would have nodded when she walked past them, stared ahead with their fixed gazes. The autumn sun had seared into her skull. But she loved the feel and the look of the raw burnt orange cotton and going to the Gurudwara gave her an excuse to wear it. Coming out from beneath the skirts and blouses it was crumpled and looked like a rag. It needed to be pressed. Under the scalding iron it became soft and warm to touch and the steam sent a comforting whiff around the room.

Back upstairs she struggled to pull off her jeans. Then she slipped on the cotton salvaar. The salvaar with its softness and space allowed her to breathe properly. The thought that jeans, the symbol of freedom, were actually tight and cumbersome fleeted through her mind. She turned to face the mirror. Her recently cut fringe sat defiantly on her forehead and the old women in the Gurudwara would notice it. To avoid this she pinned it neatly back. She took the duppatta and placed it over her head. In the mirror reflected back at her was an image of soft religious femininity. She smiled at herself thinking that if only people knew that she had argued in the school Debating Society that conventional marriage was a form of female prostitution.

Somewhere an emptiness entered her and the smile left. It wasn't as if school made her feel better. Girls in her class commented on her life, *why can't you go out, wear short skirts, cut your hair, why do you have to do what your parents say, why do you put up with it. Why? Why? Why!* She remembered this and felt the uneasiness of being packed into tight cellophane and put on display in a museum under odd Asian cultures. But she thought a museum would refer to the display as *The Asian Way of Life In Modern Britain.*

Downstairs her mother was waiting for her, car keys in her hand and looking elegant in her sari. She, too, usually wore trousers. Her parents had moved to the suburbs, when her mother had been promoted to the level of staff-nurse. They'd wanted to give their only child Ranjit a good start in life but it had meant leaving behind the safety of the familiar.

The empty suburban streets replaced by groups of boys playing, old men, their turbans off centre, intently discussing something or other and young girls, duppattas stretching to their feet, deep in conversation. Ranjit saw shop windows piled high with tomatoes, spices and stainless steel pots and pans. Bold letters on shop window advertising cheap phone rates to India, Pakistan, Karachi, followed by more shops selling pomegranates and spinach, followed by a shop called Dhulan Ki Khuchi selling glitter and gold, made Ranjit feel snug as a small child in a warm bed. The car turned into St John's Road and stopped outside an old sandstone mansion with Welcome To Guru Nanak Gurudwara painted on the front. Her mother opened the car door and Ranjit realised how hot it had been in the car.

Outside there were groups of people coming out of the Gurudwara and others about to go in. Ranjit watched a balding elderly man talking to a young couple and a child. The adults were talking quickly and Ranjit could see the rapid excitement of absorbed conversation. Sometimes the mother would lean over to the child and say something and then would return to the adults. It looked as if the conversation rambled on and had no beginning or end and the child stood limply by his parents' sides. Ranjit knew the post-Gurudwara feeling, both as an adult and as a child. As a child, happy at first, then bored. As an adult over-fed and maniacally excited. Ranjit's mother was already getting out so Ranjit stopped staring and stepped out of the car, pulling her duppatta tightly over her head, making sure that her fringe was neatly tucked beneath the hair grips. She felt awkward and cold.

Suddenly Mahinder Masee appeared, walking toward them, her voice booming, 'At last you're here!'

She enveloped Ranjit with a large hug. Ever since she had been a little girl Mahinder Masee had served as a refuge from the taunts and discomfort in Ranjit's new school in the suburbs. She'd told Ranjit that if the children ever again said that she smelled of curry she was to tell them that it was better than smelling as if they'd never washed after a shit.

Ranjit of course had never dared say anything but knowing that her aunt thought she had a right to say it had given her courage. Meanwhile her mother used to tell Ranjit to ignore the other children.

Mahinder Masee and women like her with their freshly

washed, ironed, wind-blown salvaar kameeza gave Ranjit
strength. These women believed what they knew and knew
what they believed. They'd come as unwelcome outsiders to
this country and twenty years later they had survived intact.

All three women walked towards the Gurudwara. Inside
the temple Ranjit felt an instantaneous recognition, as if a light
had just been switched on. The smell of scalding chappattis and
incense, the heat and bright colours of the women's salvaar
kameeza, the red carpeted hall, the activity, enveloped her in an
invisible warm embrace. With the buzz of chat and children's
voices in the background she climbed the soft stairs to enter the
room upstairs. A bearded man sat beneath the orange, red and
gold canopy reading in a low lyrical tone from the Guru
Granth. She didn't understand a word of Gurmukhi but a peace
entered her belly. Alongside lay the tabla and harmonica and
two men sat cross-legged waiting to begin the singing. Ranjit
felt glad. She'd been coming to this Gurudwara since she could
remember.

She settled herself cross-legged on the floor with the other
women in the gathering and became absorbed into the silent
atmosphere of harmony. Some time passed and then as if someone had jabbed her with a stick, she remembered to check her
forehead for loose hair. She glanced around her to see if anyone
had noticed.

When they had eaten, Ranjit and her mother went to
Masee's house for an after-Gurudwara cup of hot tea before
they returned to the suburbs.

The back room in Masee's house trebled and quadrupled
into a room for sitting watching television, for sleeping at night,
for entertaining, for peeling vegetables while watching
Neighbours, for ironing or whatever else needed done. Ranjit
thought of this room as more than just a room, it welcomed you,
it didn't demand any special, appropriate behaviour from you.

Two elderly women were already in the back room, one
crumpled on the sofa while the other sat on the floor leaning
her head against the wall. They talked and interrupted each
other whenever they felt like it as well as laughing and picking
their noses or teeth with great ease. Ranjit recognised them as
two of the many members of Masee's extended family. A faint
smell of yesterday's kerala cooking still sparked in the air.

Immediately Ranjit felt as if a place in the jigsaw was waiting for her to fill it.

'Come and sit beside me, beti,' called Masee's mother-in-law.
Ranjit sat beside her while her Masee went to make chai.
The older women asked her what she was studying and eyed her
with curiosity and appreciation. Looking at her smooth skin
and slimness made them feel older; it reminded them of their
youth. Then they commented on how thin she was and told her
to eat more with loud voices full of mischief.

The mother-in-law said, 'Remember Basanti, she was like a
stick when she got married and now look at her.'

The woman leaning against the wall slowly shook her head
and added, 'that husband of hers is no good, running off with
other women. It was a bad storm on her wedding day, roofs
blowing off, cows running wild.'

The mother-in-law replied distractedly, 'It was the best milk
for miles, our village had the best cows, the best milk.'

Ranjit was fascinated by this world so long ago and so far
away. The world where milk came from cows instead of cartons
in Tesco's.

Her aunt brought in the tea and the room filled with the
contented sipping of the milky cardamom-flavoured drink.
Ranjit noticed Masee's mother-in-law's eyes peering question-
ingly at Ranjit.

'Beti,' she said, 'have you been cutting your hair at the front?'

Ranjit felt as if she'd just been hit by a ball and when she
recovered she nodded. She knew she couldn't exactly say no,
especially when sharp ends of hair were sticking out now that
she wasn't wearing the duppatta.

The silence was broken by Masee's voice, 'Ranjit, I know it's
hard in this country but you do know that the old gurus sacri-
ficed so much for us so that we could live as we chose, and all
that they asked was that we do not cut a hair from our body.'

After this the room felt too big, like there was too much
space between people. The women continued talking and
Ranjit heard bits of conversation and laughter. She was glad
when it was time to go.

When Ranjit was busy putting on her coat Mahinder Masee
pushed a brown greasy bag into Ranjit's hand saying, 'Here take
these, you didn't get a chance to taste my fish pakora, eat them
tomorrow.'

Ranjit gave a small smile and said 'Thanks,' and got into the
car. She just wanted to be away from there.

From within the speeding car, Ranjit watched the street

pass by with its scattered empty paper bags and boxes of rotting vegetables.

When she got home she put the bag with pakoras into the kitchen cupboard; she didn't want to be reminded.

At lunchtime, the next day at school, girls exchanged stories about love-bites and who got off with whom. Ranjit didn't have much to say, they would just look at her if she spoke about the old ladies or her aunt and the Gurudwara.

Anyway she had her fringe right over her forehead this morning, so she sat and laughed when they laughed, frowned when they frowned and looked interested when they looked interested.

At lunchtime the school buzzed with overgrown pupils. Ranjit heard someone shout an insult meant for her. She was the only brown-skinned person in the school. She tried to not bother about it but the feeling that she'd been punched in the head just wouldn't go away. So she decided to get out of school and sit in the park and eat her lunch. When she opened her lunch box there was the brown bag of pakoras next to the cheese sandwiches. Her mother must have slipped them in when Ranjit wasn't looking. When she took a bite of the pakora the tangy spices and besan slithered and jolted through her body. Ahead she saw the clear dark lines of the tree trunks and branches and the autumn leaves ready to fall for winter.

Glossary

Salvaar kameez – Punjabi tunic and trousers
Gurudwara   – Sikh temple
Duppatta   – long scarf worn with salvaar kameez
Guru Granth   – Sikh Holy Book
Gurmukhi   – ancient dialect used in scriptures and poetry
Masee   – mother's sister
Kirtan   – religious songs and music
Kerala   – Asian vegetable (bitter gourd)
Beti   – daughter; affectionate term used to address
                a young woman
Besan   – chick-pea flour

Olive M. Ritch

A POEM FOR EDWIN

You're standing at ease
in the garden
smiling at me
from the sepia photograph.

I am surprised
by your height
and handsome features
unlike your brother,

my grandfather,
who was short and stumpy
with hands like shovels
to work the land.

I want to take you
back to my house
and frame you,
not leave you lying

in a box
in my uncle's attic.
You should see
the light of day

and not be feared
or forgotten. You can do
no harm to me, the child
you never knew.

I was born
three months after
you measured the rope
in the garden shed.

Leaving no note
for me to read,
just the silence
in the shadows.

James Robertson

NOTES FAE 'CREATIVE WRITING IN SCOTS': THE HAIKU

I'll gie him ...

A Scots haiku eh?
Crummie thocht, pechin tae the
Tap o Schiehallion.

Why haiku?

If they want tae mak
Whisky, hou can we no tak
A blad fae their buik?

Streetch an bend

Dinna get fankelt.
Luik – it's juist an exercise.
Like touchin yer taes.

Get it richt

Less o yer English
Nonsense, missus, an mair o
Yer clishmaclaivers.

Makkin an erse o't

It's no easy, ken,
Trying tae scrieve some o thae
Wee bahookie hings.

Oot o line

Oh ay, there's ayewis
Yin. Winna dae as he's tellt.
Breenges in wi baith buits disna listen niver lairns thinks
       he kens it aw...

April Simmons

RAY

We may have built the Tamar Bridge between us but there is still something pretty odd at the western end of it –
Western Morning News

They say I was dropped on my head the day I was born. I don't remember it, but then I don't remember much really. It's not that nothing goes in up here or that it sneaks off as soon as it arrives, but more like everything I see and hear gets in and then decides it'll stay for a little swim. My dad says if you listen very close when your head is in the bathwater you can hear it rattling inside like loose pipes. And he's right. It's a wonder I reached this birthday with it rattling round so hard.

The pigeons are scratching the roof and one or other of the tellies is on underneath. Me, when I'm not watching the telly I like to lie on my bed here and think. I can never remember what I'm thinking about but I know it's always something so interesting I can't take my eyes off the wall. Lots of cars go past the house and I reckon I think about them a fair bit, though it's hard to say if they're going out of Cornwall or further down. I like to think they're going out. Being on the main road gets you thinking like that, but even when I'm thinking hard I can feel dad and Aunt Ruby moving about underneath and it makes me all warm inside knowing my family's nearby, especially when we've got the same programme on. Sometimes I turn my volume right down to see if we have. They're both a bit deaf, but when Aunt Ruby is drinking she likes to wallow in the sound. Then I have to walk to the end of the room and poke my head down through the hole so I can hear dad's. A day like today when the sun is all over the floor I might stay and watch telly or give my pigeons a bit of cheese, but seeing as it's my birthday I'm obliged to visit, dad says.

I go out the back door and round the yard to the side door for Aunt Ruby. I have to squish flat to get round the side. Dad pays a lady to do the shopping for her; says I'd come back with soup if she wanted spinach, and that's a relief or she'd have me buying her brandy. Aunt Ruby and her brandy, they're like a baby and milk. 'We go back a long way,' she says, but not long enough to go out her door for it. Dad says last time she went

out was three years ago and that was only because she thought
it was the door to her bathroom, she were that pissed. Aunt
Ruby's door has glass in it with sailing boats and I can see the
colours from the telly, but I can't see what's on. The walls are
pink and the ceiling is pink and I can see that too. From the
inside she can see me squished against the glass, a big fine boy,
she always says.

'Call back later, dear, I'm doing the tidying,' Aunt Ruby says
this time.

She's in bed still.

I walk round the back of the house and squish up the other
side and round the front to dad's bit. The van takes up all the
garden and I have to make myself dirty when I squish past the
van to get to the door. It is a nice tidy garden and Dad's crocuses are growing round the wheels. The van is white and shiny,
but dad can't clean the side because the step ladder doesn't fit.
Before the van it was the caravan and the side of that was dirty
too. It was a blow for dad having to move indoors but it was
the nosebleeds what did it. Doctors are sadists, he says, stuffing
people's noses right up the top without even knocking them out
first. Now he sleeps bolt up in the armchair to keep the blood
in, but he still has the idea of taking off. One day when it is
sunny and he is feeling well he will take off, he says. One day
when the van's done.

I press the white button. My dad opens the door, his hair is
very combed and white and he is extra tidy today. He says it's
because of my birthday. He holds his hand out straight. I pull
my hand out the pocket and stick it at him.

'Not that one.'

He gives it a little slap. It's a game. 'Sorry Sir,' I say and want
to giggle.

We go in his room all smelling of the kippers what my dad
likes to eat. The bed is in the middle with the settee and arm-
chairs all round it, 'just in case they come to take me away,' he
says. If you sit on the settee you have to put your legs on the
bed and dad doesn't like that so I'm standing up. That woman
is on the telly again. 'Nothing but the bloody election,' dad says
and puts it on the other side.

He gives me a brown envelope and tells me to open it. In it
is a little blue book. It has lots of numbers inside.

'Take a good hard look, Ray,' he says. 'That's all yours.'

Dad gives me this little blue book every time I get my birthday and then he takes it off me and puts it in the sideboard. I would like to have that little blue book in my room because dad keeps his curtains across so he can't see the dirty side of the van. There's boxes on the floor and they've all got white stickers on them. The mantelpiece has got jars with white stickers and the sideboard has got brown envelopes with white stickers. In the envelopes are all my dad's receipts for 30 years, the shopper woman says. She calls him a silly goat.

'Thanks,' I say.

I said it right. He is pleased and he goes to the sideboard and puts something in a glass that isn't brandy. He hits my glass with his glass.

'Cheers,' we say. I want to giggle. The something smells too much and my eyes cry by themselves. But it tastes alright. I put my finger in and lick a bit and then I put my glass on the sideboard by the big brown envelopes.

On the telly is the man what was blown up in the car park last week and lots of people bringing flowers there to London, but there's no sound. I'd like to go to London. We can hear a quiz programme through the hardboard where the door to Aunt Ruby's was before.

'Clark Gable,' Aunt Ruby shouts at the telly. There's lots of clapping.

'What about your Aunt?' dad says.

'She's doing the tidying,' I say.

'In bed. At this time?' he says and looks at one of the clocks on the wall. 'You saw her yesterday, I suppose. How is her room?'

'Alright,' I say. We can hear her knocking.

'Can you see the floor?'

I think hard. 'Not really,' I say. 'But she's doing the tidying.'

Dad thinks a bit. He says, 'She's waiting. You'd better go round.'

Then he says, 'Now listen. I've got to tell you something first.'

All the time we can hear knocking.

*

Aunt Ruby gives me a card. It doesn't have an envelope. She's lost it, she says. On the table in her room there's magazines, there's pens, there's postcards, there's powder puffs, there's hankies, there's bottle-lids, there's curlers, there's corks. There's Christmas cards and a little telly and dirty glasses and spilt-out matches and clip-ons for her ears and plant-pots with nothing in them, and there's an envelope for the card on the arm of the chair.

'Look at the picture,' she says. 'Look.'

I look hard. It is a blue and red boat on a yellow beach. At the top it says '30'. The '3' is in gold. The '0' is in orange felt-tip. A little bit in the corner is soft and bendy and smells of Aunt Ruby's brandy. 'It's nice,' I say.

Today Aunt Ruby is all smiles. Her lips and her cheeks are the same red, but it's redder in the cracks and on her teeth. Round her eyes it's blue and that's gone bluer in the cracks as well. She's wearing a shiny red frock and red glass in her ears and pearls down her front. Her shoes are red today and her hair is orange.

'Open it. Open it,' she says.

I open it. A pound drops on the floor. It is soft and worn and stuck together in the middle. I go down and put it in my pocket.

'Don't tell your dad,' she whispers.

'Alright,' I say.

'Read what it says inside. Read it to me.'

'It says 'Happy Birthday, Ray,' I say.

'Anything else?'

I can't read it but I know what it says, the same as it always says when I get my birthday. 'It says 'With love from your Aunt Ruby',' I tell her.

'I can hardly believe it,' Aunt Ruby says and takes a glass off the table and cleans it inside with a hankie. Then she takes another one and gives it to me. She puts in the brandy. 'Cheers,' we say and hit our glasses and drink a bit. Aunt Ruby finishes hers and waits for me and then we have some more.

'Thanks,' I say.

'I sent the woman out for it,' Aunt Ruby says. 'I told her it had to be a boat, a bright jolly boat, because it's in our blood. Of course you don't live by the sea like I did, but look, it's got a bell on it and a life-ring. Do you like the colour? It's marvellous.'

We look at the card for a long time. Aunt Ruby gets her lipstick off the table. She puts it on her mouth the same way she rubs a match on its box, one way, then another way, and then she wipes some on her finger and rubs it round her cheeks. Her rouge has been run out for more than a month, she says, but the shopper woman doesn't get what she asks for off the list. I want to tell Aunt Ruby the thing I've got to tell her, but she wants to talk about the card.

'Look at all those white bits in the sea,' she says. 'They call them seahorses.'

'They don't look much like it,' I say.

'No, but they ride the waves like them,' she says. 'I remember a day when the sea spilled over on the road, and it was gusty too. It looked like everything had been hung out on the line to dry. Then there was a thousand of those white horses and I lost my hat.'

'Aunt Ruby, I've got to tell you something,' I say.

We have a bit more brandy and Aunt Ruby starts on about town. She hates our town because it's too far east and she can't see the sea from her window like I can from my roof, but she can see people coming at her glass door and I can't see that.

'What's on telly?' I ask her.

Aunt Ruby starts looking for the telly paper. 'I mustn't miss my programme,' she says, raking round on the table and knocking things on the floor. Sometimes she sweeps everything except the telly off the table, and then for days after she keeps breaking stuff when she walks across the room.

'I've got to be getting back to my pigeons,' I tell her quick and stand up.

*

The van is nearly ready. Not long to go now, dad says. You'll be the man of the house, he says, you have to tell Aunt Ruby. But Aunt Ruby doesn't want to hear what I've got to tell her and I'm coming home. My knees are soft and Aunt Ruby holds me a bit to the door before she closes it and goes back in to watch telly. 'Cheerio,' I say.

The sky is going round in circles and the house wall keeps hitting me onto the other wall. When I get to the yard I keep an eye on the washing line. I hold tight to the house wall and go in my door quick. The ladder doesn't want to stop for me so I sit on the bottom for a time. My insides are making funny noises and my mouth feels wet but I want to sit by the ladder and put my head down. When I put my head up it's already dark and I can't see proper. The pigeons'll be hungry with me not seeing to them all day but I want to lie on my own bed and close my eyes.

I keep it really nice up here even when it's going round in circles. I've got lumps on my head where I bang it on the roof but I keep it really nice and, like dad says, I haven't got anything to hurt. But I've got the bed and a camping fridge and an oven. I keep things in a big box the telly come in, things dad and Aunt Ruby give me. Other than that I've got my telly which I keep on top of the box. The shopper woman doesn't like me watching telly, she says to me 'Go out more,' but I don't have to, not me. I don't have to get all dressed up and go down the pub on Friday night, worrying if I might get my head kicked in and whether I'll meet a girl who'll be willing to come home with me. Or how I'll fit her in my bed if she does. I hear them coming down the road shouting and singing and breaking things, clip-clop shoes and bad language, and I put my head under the blanket thankful I'm in here with just my hole in the floor and window in the roof.

From this roof you can see where town finishes and the road goes on. I reckon that's why the pigeons like to live here. If I go and open this window it's like you can hear what all the town's doing. The wind is making my face cold and my head feels very loose, but there's lots of stars. I can see the neighbours' houses and the top of dad's van. Someone's shouting somewhere and there's lots of cars going past still, all going to the same place by the looks of it, but I can't remember if that's the road out or the road in. My head is feeling looser and looser and I don't know if dad's van will go the way they're going anymore.

*

Someone's shouting. I put the blanket back and go over to the window in the roof. The sun is well up and my head is hurting more than when I bang it. I go to my hole. The shouting is coming from underneath. I've got to put my clothes back on quick. I climb down the ladder and go out the back door. A big pink sheet is in the way of the wall. I want to squish past the big pink sheet, but my head gets wet and I can't see.

When I get out I'm not by the house anymore but right in the yard. I follow the wall back to the corner of the house. Aunt Ruby's door is open.

Inside there's a bucket and that's bad news because it means it's Aunt Ruby's clean-up day. Aunt Ruby says there's no use having a clean-up day because the room is full of bottles and the dustbin men won't take them, but the shopper woman still comes Mondays. The people on the telly are shouting about the government. Aunt Ruby is shouting to the shopper woman. 'He was absolutely delighted with it,' she shouts. 'He kept on looking at it. He could hardly believe it. He kept opening and closing it and looking at the colours. He was thrilled.'

I am going to go away again but the shopper woman comes into this bit and looks at me where I am in the door.

'That telly is very loud,' I say like my dad.

The shopper woman makes her eyes roll round and goes back into Aunt Ruby's room.

Aunt Ruby is not watching the telly. She's standing in the middle of her room because the bed hasn't got any covers on it and she's still in her blue nightie and dressing gown with a bottle in her hand. She's got blue stuff on her eyes, and she's got on pink cheeks and pink lipstick. Someone is knocking the wall.

'It's Ray,' I shout.

The shopper woman has got the hoover on and she's hoovering round Aunt Ruby. The lead is going round and round Aunt Ruby's blue slippers so the shopper woman stands up and moves Aunt Ruby in the corner. Aunt Ruby comes back again. She is holding her bottle like it's a little baby animal.

'I'm telling dad on you,' I shout.

'I'm thirsty. There's no lemonade,' she shouts.

'And that'll help your thirst,' the shopper woman shouts and puts Aunt Ruby in the corner. Aunt Ruby comes back again.

'Can you believe it,' she shouts. 'I had shoes of every style and shade, and I had as many lipsticks as I had shoes.'

'No,' I say.

The banging is getting more. An ornament falls off the telly. A duck falls off the wall.

'Listen,' Aunt Ruby shouts. 'He's a fine one, what with all those kippers,' but the shopper woman goes to the telly and turns the knob. The telly stops.

'Aunt Ruby. I've got to tell you something,' I say.

'There's no need to shout,' says Aunt Ruby. She puts on the telly. It's the programme with the big funny people now. They're holding buckets and going through the mud, and I like this programme more than anything.

'Aunt Ruby. He's off,' I tell her, keeping an eye on the funny people.

'Off?' she shouts.

'He says he's off and I'll be the man of the house. He says.'
Aunt Ruby laughs loud and has a bit of brandy.

'The van's nearly done.'

'The van's always nearly done,' Aunt Ruby shouts.

'That van's been nearly done for five years,' the shopper
woman shouts and puts off the telly. The banging stops as well.

'It's really nearly done this time,' I tell them. 'He says when
the crocuses are gone he'll be off. And he said for me to tell
you.'

Aunt Ruby puts the telly back on. The funny people are in
the water. I want to go up to my room with the hole in the
floor and the roof window and watch the funny people in the
water. 'I've got to be getting back to my pigeons,' I say, and go
out the door.

Kirsty Smith

MARS BAR

'If you don't finish writing then you won't do any sewing!' yelled Mrs Blair.

'Well, that's that bollocked up,' said Chunk, folding his worksheet into a paper aeroplane. I did the same. Everyone hates sewing. And if we don't do writing we don't get sewing. So no-one does the writing. And I mean no-one. Not one person. The most we write is our name and class at the top of the sheet.

My pal, Chunk. Been pals with him since day one of high school. He was standing all by himself outside Science at playtime. I gave him a Mars Bar which is our favourite sweet. Then he came over to play footie with us.

He might sound fat but Chunk's not actually fat. In first year he was so huge that the councils were trying to buy him to build houses on. Anyway, during the summer his mum put him on a crash diet, after which he looked like a broomstick.

Everyone in the class copies us two. Wants to be our pals. They definitely don't want to be our enemies like Mrs Blair.

Me and Chunk, we're the leaders of 2.11. Everyone takes their lead from us.

I'm the best in Home Ecs. Like the time Mrs Blair (from the Blair Witch Project as we sometimes called her) said we weren't going to cook, I began yelling 'We want to cook!' which the whole class took up. Mrs Blair ran out in tears with us throwing eggs after her as she went out the door and us all cheering. She shouldn't be a teacher if she can't hack it so we don't feel guilty. I don't anyway.

A paper plane hit me on the side of the head. I looked over and saw Clarry Simpson grinning at me. 'Right,' I said picking up the plane. 'This means war!'

Five minutes later there was chaos. Planes flying everywhere and Mrs Blair in the middle of it. I wondered if she'd run out crying again. Beside me Chunk murmured 'A Mars Bar if she goes out greeting.'

'Bet she doesnae.'

Five minutes later, I owed Chunk a Mars Bar.

Gerry Stewart

INTIMACY

She is left lying, exposed on the bed
while he gets up to paint this moment.
He ignores the stark distance he creates
between her and the easel. Passion
has been displaced by the artist stilling time.

She has been caught in her habit of sleeping
curled like the dried husk of a milkweed pod.
Light trickles along her, spreading across the sheets
until it pours into a pool on the red carpet.
Gentle shadows gather at her arm
where he once slept.

Liam Stewart

NEW BOOK

Me and Pete never talked to Maggie McPhie in the playground. Except for fuck off when we were playing football
and they were hanging on to the railings laughing at us. Her
and Gina and Alice Hardie. Shouting things. 'She wants to gie
you your hole.' Stuff like that.

It's a photy-finish between Maggie and Ronnie Shannon
for who's the dumbest. When Floody's out the room you can
hear him going round the classrooms. Like a polis horse with
his steel heels. Clippety clip, clippety clip. It echoes right up
the well and hits the glass dome. But Ronnie cannae work it
out. Clip clip clippety clip, and he's two doors down at Miss
Carson's. His sandpapery voice cuts through the air. 'A lovely
time in Wester Ross... bla... bla... bla.' The laugh rattles out
her as if he's shook her. The door closes and then clip clip clippety clip and he by-passes Old McKinstry's room. Only speaks
to her through notes. Clip clip clippety clip, and here he comes
wheeling right into the room on his wee bandy legs, buttoning
up his double-breaster and shouting.

'Shannon, just stay out son. McPhie, join him. He's got
nothing up top. You're worse for laughing.'

He trots over to his high desk and flings the lid up. Floody's
wee pal comes into action. None of the thin, dark coiled-up
kind. It's toffee-coloured and it's that thick you can hardly fold
it. It stands right up itself as soon as he lifts it above his head.
And Floody definitely can draw it. It's a laugh seeing Ronnie.
He dances about, tiptoe to tiptoe with his mouth open, but
still managing to keep his hands presented the way you've got
to. Whizz! Cerrack! Like a rifle shot. Right on target! Wee
Ronnie writhes about as if he's been wounded. He's funny
with his wee bendy ears, sucking in his mouth, even when he's
doing his sums. But it's murder trying not to laugh when he's
getting the belt. His hands squirm about between his legs like
wee kittens. 'Up again!' You've got to put them out crossed
again within about ten seconds or he grabs you by the wrist
and just keeps lashing into your hand till he's knackered. The
second smash and Ronnie twitches across the floor making a
face like the hunchback of Notre Dame. Your stomach's that
sore, it's murder. If you make a sound, Floody would yank you

out to the floor no hesitation. Once his arm's swinging, he wants as many things to hit as he can get.

At the first lash, Maggie howls like an Alsatian. The hair at the back of your neck tingles. At the second, it's as if somebody's murdered her. Ronnie carries his hands back to his desk like injured pigeons. Sits there rocking backwards and forwards comforting them. Maggie bubbles and squeezes her fingers like washing, looking down to see if the pain's going to drip out.

Maggie smells as well. The whole three of them in fact. Old McKinstry was a laugh that first day we got her. She turns round from the board. 'Is there somebody in here wearing an unfresh garment?' she says. Then she asks them point blank. Along the front row. Maggie, Gina, Alice Hardie. It could be any of them. They all say no miss! 'Well,' she says, getting back to the chalk, 'someone is. And I would advise whoever it is to have the garment changed during the lunch-break.'

Maggie smells like a mixture of fags and sweat and that thick smell you get off all the McPhies, their wee house with the big pan of fat always melting and hardening and melting again. Her face is as brown as a suntan and she's got rosy cheeks and grey eyes. Old McKinstry in that daft tartan skirt. She puts her hands on her pelvis and says to Maggie, 'you know, Margaret, if you were to tidy yourself up and have a good wash, you could be quite a bonny girl.'

Her brother smelt the same and had the same burnt cheeks. He was in the class above us. Billy McPhie. He had an amazing clump of red hair and he always had on the same bottle-green jersey. He was an even bigger dumbo than Maggie. When the heidie read out their qualy marks, he got an M. Mental. He went about the playground telling everybody, breathing into his hand and rubbing it across his heart. But you didnae mess with Billy. There was a wall at the end of our playground about eight feet high with a garage and scrapyard on the other side full of amazing battered wrecks of cars. If you got caught on top of the wall, you got sent to the heidie. Billy was the only one that could be up there and back down before a teacher could see him. He ran along the top like a monkey just to give you a laugh.

It was Billy that gave me my worst summer holidays. I was still pale-faced by the end of August. But my ma says, it's no use missing your schooling. It was the bad dreams. His hand circling and circling, clawing the air. Green and red, and the river-bed rushing towards them.

Farley from our class's da is the janny at the posh school across the big bridge on Great Western Road. Sometimes you can sook in with him to get invited over to play with him. He's got a brilliant bedroom, with aquariums and everything.

He tries to say he was there when it happened. But he's a wee liar, trying to sook in with you cos he's got a weak bladder and he's supposed to get running out the class whenever he wants. Floody didn't like that arrangement so he let him pee himself two or three times before the wee janny went to the heidie to complain. Now he lets him go just in time.

Big Murphy was with Billy when it happened. He's never been back at school since, but his pal Skelley got the story off him. Murphy had to tell the story to the polis a whole lot of times.

They had went into the new extension getting built at the posh school, and they had walked about up in the beams and burst the big bags of plaster with batons of wood. At least Billy had walked the beams. Big Murphy admitted he had to pull himself along on the crotch, horsey-back style. Then, according to Skelley, wee Farley's da appeared and they had to dodge him round the plaster bags before they could get running out. He shouted after them that he's going to report them to the heidie after the holidays. Big Murphy shouted, 'yer granny's a cowboy' and Billy shouted, 'away and take a wank to yersel.' They werenae worried because they were finished with the primary school.

They were still laughing by the time they got to the big bridge. 'The bam's a spastic, same as his boy,' wee Billy says. Then they flung stones down at the ducks with the green heads, miles below them, swimming about. A woman gied them a row. Then big Murphy knocks on the top of the metal parapet thing. 'Bet you cannae walk along that, Billy.' And, of course, Billy's up the next minute, gliding along it with his arms out like a tight-rope walker. It wasn't till somebody shouted that he lost his balance. And then his hand went round and round in a circle, and he fell over.

His fingers are trying to hook into the air. And the river-bed's accelerating at him, his red hair and his green jersey. But that's my dream, because big Murphy didnae say any of that to Skelley, because he ran away as soon as Billy's hand started to go round in a circle.

BOY FALLS SEVENTY FEET TO HIS DEATH the paper said. My ma and da sat looking at it, then at me, then back again at the paper. It had a big picture of the bridge and a broken white arrow to show you where he fell and where he hit the river. I woke up and screamed just when the boulders were going to smash into me.

One good thing about going back to school is you get your new books. The first day Floody sends us running about with piles of books for the other classes. I stagger into Old McKinstry's room with a stack of blue No Lumber History books. She takes one look at them and says, 'We're not soiling our hands with books in that condition. Just you take them back to Mr Flood and tell him they are unacceptable.' Pete's the same with the orange No Lumber Geography. Unacceptable.

Floody's beelin. 'Leave them against the wall,' he shouts and slams the door shut. It'll be a big fight later on. Just to show he's got standards himself he goes through the bundle of the Radiant Reading Book Seven and lobs three or four of the scabbiest on the window ledge. They're that tattered they fall apart before they land. Then he counts out the exact number for the class and nods at me to hand them out. The thought of getting my hands on a new reading book makes my stomach jittery. Floody's grating away about what he'll do to people that don't get their books covered, so he doesnae see Maggie dipping into her bag and pulling out a Radiant Reading Book Seven.

She gives me a wee shy look and places it in front of her. 'I've got one,' she says.

I hand the extra one back to Floody. 'Oh did I not count right?' he says, trying to smile.

'Sir, Margaret McPhie already had one.'

'Already had one?' He's upset with this. His forehead crowds into the middle. He walks over and picks up Maggie's book, turns it over as if it's a clue in a murder mystery. 'Where on earth did you get this book girl?' he says. You would think it was the weirdest thing that ever happened to him in his whole life.

'Sir... sir...,' Maggie says, 'it was in my bag.' She's got a bad habit of keeping her head down when she's talking to teachers. It drives Floody mad. The grey bags under his eyes turn pink.

'What are you doing with a school book in your bag?' he shouts.

Every hand backs away from the new Radiant Reading. Not a rustle.

Maggie nibbles at her mouth, like a rabbit at a bit of straw. It still sounds like, 'sir... sir... sir,' but you can hardly hear it.

'For God's sake, girl, would you speak up!'

'Sir... sir... sir... it was my brother's.'

'Your brother's? What on earth are you doing with your brother's book?' Now he's really shouting. 'Why didn't he return it himself?'

Nobody says anything. Maggie's bubbling.

'What school has he gone to? Do you think you can just pass on school property as if it was your own? What's your brother's name?'

Was. Was. Was. It was Billy McPhie. Nobody says it or tries to put their hand up.

'Sir... sir... sir... sir.'

Then Floody loses it. He smashes the Radiant Reading on to the desk. 'Would you speak up. What is your brother's name?'

'Sir... sir... sir... sir.'

He jumps at his desk. Cracks the lid hinges. The wee pal leaps into his hand. Up in the air. He grabs Maggie's wrist and starts leathering into her. 'You damn chirping brat. I'll make you speak up!' he's roaring. Batter! Batter! Batter!

She screams. A hand's going round and round. I'm clawing the air. I'm in a green jersey. The river rushing up at me. A voice shouts out. 'He's dead! He's dead! He's dead! He fell off the bridge.'

Floody's angry face is pointed at me. He's like something you've surprised and it might attack you. He unlocks Maggie's wrist and she drops to the floor whimpering. His wee pal's hanging limp. 'He's dead?' he says in a growly whisper. 'Dead?'

Before he notices, Maggie's up and out the door. He's still glaring at me, muttering something I can't hear. When he sees her empty desk, he trots over to the banister and shouts, 'Margaret! Margaret!' in the voice he usually keeps for Miss Carson.

In the afternoon, we're stifling in the classroom. Floody sends me for the window pole. He's watching me over the top of his grey pouches with a funny look in his eyes. My arms are trembling that much I cannae get the hook into the ring. He knows the whole story now. Something'll happen. I clatter the pole against the glass and tense up for one of his blasts. It clunks home at last and I squeak it down eighteen inches.

Maggie's not back after dinner-time.

He's poking a map of the British Isles with a pointer, but still trying to make his sandpapery voice sound mild. And there's something else, something unusual about Floody, as if he's not finding it easy to keep our attention. All the time, we're watching the door out the corner of our eyes.

A trapped wasp's bouncing off a window pane. If I had seen Maggie at dinner-time I would have said bring your ma up. The wasp whips away from the window, sweeps across our heads, then back to the window panicking to get out. Floody places the pointer against the wall and clips across to his desk. He rolls his paper into a baton and goes to the window. I can see his teeth are gritted when he's crushing the wasp. He wants to make sure it's definitely dead.

He's some bastard, Floody.

Sam Trainor

REVOLVER

At thiyend o th day thiyole thing wz all just about startin owva. There wz nuthin forit, woz th. Shid just aff t puddidall biyoind her n geddon with livin outa loif. Theyad no roight tuwuv left her loik this that way. Th twofaced bastuds. Evrywonud screwd her owva. Turna. Th solisituz. Th Press. Evrythin wz black n whoit t them. Evrybudy tht shid went to when she needid elp'd just change jsoids loik thad overnoit. Thed ad er backwoods and forwoods t Jamayca loik a bleedin pingpong ball; n then thed dropt her roight between th devil n th deep blue sea withoud a word. So Eleanor wz just another case these days. The Eleanor O Neale case. It wz all she could do t troy and show that she wz really human. Make a change. Shid have t stick idall behoind her n geddon withit.

Eleanor O Neale'd pud herself about, thats what thi sed; an it wz all too bloody obvious. *All mouth and no knickuz* as her mom would say – though *she* wz nobudy t tork – or wz it *all knickuz and no mouth*. That wz a nasty little turn of phrase that now she came t think aboud it, really nasty. Though her mom wz roight uz far uz anywon could tell though. Eleanor could probly say shid slep with evry pistup blowk who'd eva pistup th back o th Traf on a Froiday noit, and they could definitely all say thed slep with her. There wz no two waysuv lookin addit when ya looktadit loik that.

Eleanor'd yoosta rattle on loik there wz no tomorra. Back when th woulduv bin thadiz. Shid come out with more little catchphrases than you could shake a stick at; she made a point uvit, loik they wz gowin ouda fashn. It wz loik shid come up with th phrase *to doin out on somethin* n wz gunna do just that withit until th cows came owm if it killda. And she sed she ad this penpal in Rowm (loik she eva rowt) – sometoims it wz Idaho, she alwiz loik th sownd of Idaho, it sortuv rowld off th tung so t speak – n this wummn could literally talk thiyoind legs offa donkey. Eleanor towld stranjuz this in boozas, loik a drunk Irishman lets ya sniffiz whiskey t see its mowstly water. Sumthin loik thad anyway. But now she wuznt sayin nuthin. She couldnt. She wz still. Not wantin t disturb.

When she got back owm shid buy erself a little owse in Water Orton – somewhere noice loik that. She ad sum money from th deal with Th Mirror leftowva. Shid gederself a whole lowda soffurnishins stuff from th catalog. You could phown owt these days. No need t go t town t go t town. Shid gedda loada rugs n throws n stuff. And shid buy one eachuv evry sortuv bedlinin: them beautiful old teardrop sortuv patterns that her cuzn Suzn ad. Shid make herself a little cowsy little den where she could just curlup and doi. Forgottn. Hopefully forgotn anyway. N the bedlinin wz importnt. Fresh sheets evry day. Ispeshly when shiyad her period. If she still *godda* period when it wz worse. God that wz scary. Ass th doctor that. Moinjoo, she probly didnav two bleedin ormowns t rub tgetha azitwoz. Buddeevn so, shid put fresh sheets on evry mornin n just go back t bed n hoid.

N that poor owl cow'd bin hiddn away erself thiyowl toim they wz gowin out uzwell. Howuz Eleanor supposta know tht shid be owldup in th lowcl ospitul? Turna neva sed a thing. She knew he ad a woif though obviyusly. He neva spowk abouda, not in English anyway, but lookin back adit he did ave this attitude loik sumwon troyin tuwiscape frum sumthin. He wz obviyusly livin owt sum koinduv naughty little fantasy, th bastud. But she loikt that; so wz she. She yoosta pretend tht he wz on th run n she wz loik this moll in a sexy little oidaway. Loik Nancy in Oliva. Th tart witha hart... She couldnuv imagined.

She wz really poorly too. All that toim, all through that unbelievable toim – it made her feel sick t think aboudit. That wummn loyin ona back, skinnyuza rake, all yellowun livaspotid loik cullud people go when thi get really owld – though thi usually age betta thn uz though dont they – budit wz jus disgustin. She neva met th wummn obviyusly – what wuz she? Sum sorduva sadist? – but she could just pictura loyin in this big metal bed loik a cage, mowldin away inter th stiff whoit sheets. She knew tht she should feel sorry furra really. But how? Not just yet. She musnt. Th wummn wz loik n owld infectid plasta, she wz loik a peach thats rottn n sloimy undaneaf whenya pickidup. She wz fuckin voil.

And th sex, t think aboudit now – standin in the same owld otel room with a fuckin revolver n a leperdskin ambag loik sum sortuv trajic lowcal tart – it made th blood rush tuwa face loik she wz bare n up at altitude. And it wz dirty blood uzwell tht made her gowall red – she knew it woz – when she thought about th sex with th man in th bed in frontuva. It wz loik th water in that jar ya washed ya brushiz in ut infant school. But there wz a sortuva horrabul exoitmnt to thiyowl thing. Shid alwiz secretly smoild furra secnd ut th soituv animulz in Africa bein ript owpn n eatn aloiv frum thiyinsoid out boy big cats or whatever on th telly. It mayda shiver all owva. N Turna wz loik a big loyun now, asleep on th ded grass, or a snow leperd in them whoit sheets maybe. N t thinkabout th sex now, it wz seedy n it wz dirty. Evrythin wz rowspetulz n red woin n candleloit yknow n losin yaself init ut th start. But now she could feel th burn o th polyster sheets again n th wayvy candle-wick imprint inna bum. N she could still see th shameless cheek uv Turna puttin th face o th Virgin Mary t th wall that noit. Fuck me. That wz Turner all owva.

He mustuv dunnit delibrutly. He knew thiyowl toim unnie neva sed a fuckin thing. He never even wonce lookt justa little bid upset. He just went kinda red n horny – not th sameuz when a whoit person gz red, its more loik a darka, bluer koinduva brown – budit wz th same rushuv blood tuwiz face n iz neck uz she could feel now, hot n throttlina in thiyowtel room. N shid lettim duwit. Th big bamboo.

She wd probly neva hava nippa woodshe.

Eleanor owpund her new leperdskin hambag. It wz fake though obviyusly, she didnt really loik thiyoidiyaruv killin animulz. But she couldnt givup eatin meat: she loikt baycn too much. Thi sed th smell afta th pub bomins wz loik baycn tho. That wz inuff t put them foyermn off eatin meat furreva. She gotta sigarets out n pincht unutha shaky won outuv th pack. She litit, leavin th bag unclaspt n lookin ut th tishoos in her purse witherowld weddin ring stillin th pikchaflap, troyin tuwignor th revolver.

It wz easy inuff t gedowld ov. Too easy. Her brotha knew a blowk who knew a blowk n that wz that. Hid troid t sella battryasid. It wz what th wimmin yoozd on eachuvva roundeya, it wz grewsum. But she wz gunna killa *man*, n th goy wz appy t get th munny f th gun th trooth bi known. Shid made shewer it wz lowdid adntshe. Hid showd herow t push th round bit out n spin it round. She browk a nayul duwinit. Hid lafftata n shid sed – Om th won witha gun yknow. Hid shudup then n took th munny offa. Knew what wz good furrim. Eleanor clawd th twenytwo revolver toiter n tuchta fingerprint on th trigga delibrutly.

God Turna lookt so bloody beautiful ut thiyend o th little barrel. His face wz all still n sweet n loik a babbys. His stupid

tung powkin out; his bitsuv hair all stickinup n stickin t th
pillow wi th swet n gunk n stuff. Just loik a babby. So innosunt.
The bastud.

She couldnt neva do a thing loik that.

She pincht th fagend even toita between th top two finguz-
uva leftand.

A soun flasht distuntly betweener ears.

What wz that?

Delibrutly, she exhayuld cliyurair; sucktin bluegrey smowk;
stopta twichin lungs furra secund, still owldin th revolver.

Howldin th revolver still furra secund, t stoppa lungs twichin,
she sucktin smowk, bluegrey, n exhayuld cliyurair delibrutly.

What wz that?

A soun flasht distuntly betweener ears. She pincht th fagend
even toita. She couldnt neva do a thing loik that. So innosunt.
Just loik a babby. His bitsuv hair all stickin t th pillow wi th
swet n gunk n stuff. God Turna lookt so beautiful. Knew what
wz good furrim. Push th round bidout n spinit round. Made
shewer it wz lowdid adntshe. Battryasid. Grewsum. It wz what
th wimmin yoozd. Her brotha knewa blowk who knewa blowk
n that wz that. Owld weddin ring stillin the pikchaflap. Thi sed
th smell afta th pub bomins wz loik baycn. She didnt really loik
thiyoidearuv killin animulz. She wd probably never hava nippa
would she. Big bamboo. It wz th same rushuv blood tuwiz face
n his neck uz she could feel now hot n throttlina. Loik a darka
bluer koinduva brown. He neva sed a fuckin thing. Delibrutly.
That wz Turner all owva. Fuck me. Puttin th face o th Virgin
Mary t th wall. She could feel th burn o th polyester sheets agen
n th wayvy candlewick imprint inna bum. Everythin wz losin
yourself init ut th start. Turna wz a snow leperd. It mayda
shiverallowva. Shid alwiz secretly smoild ut animulz bein rippt
owpun n eaten aloiv frum thiyinsoid out. T think about th sex.
It wz loik th water in that jar ya wosht ya brushiz in ut infant
school. Dirty blood tht made her goowall red – she knew it woz
– when she thordabout th sex wi th man in th bed in fruntuva.
Loik she wz bare n up at altitude. Standin in th same owld otel
room with a fuckin revolver n a leperdskin ambag loik sum
sortuv trajic lowcul tart. She wz fuckin voil. Loik a peach thutz
rottn n sloimy underneath wen ya pickidup. Pikchera loyin in
this big metal bed loik a cage, mouldin away into th stiff whoit
sheets. It wz just disgustin. Loyinonna back, skinnyuza rake, all

yellowun livaspotid loik cullerd people go when thi get really
owld. It made her feel sick t think aboudit. All that toim. N she
wz really poorly too. She couldnuv imagined. She yoosta
pretend tht he wz on the run. Obviyusly livin out sum sortuv
naughty little fantasy. How wz she suppowsta know? Shid put
fresh sheets on evry mornin. If she still got a period. Shid make
herself a little cowsy little den where she could just curl up n
doi. No need t go t town t go t town. Shid buy herself a little
owse in Water Orton when she got bakowm. She woznt sayin
nothin. Eleanor'd yoosta rattlon loik there wz no tmorra. There
wz no two wayzuv lookinadit when ya looktadit loik that. Uz
far uz anywon could tell, evry pistup blowk ood eva pistup th
back o th Traf could definutly say shid slep withim. *All mouth
and no knickuz* uz her mom would say – tho she wz nowbdy t
tork. N it wz all too obviyus. Eleanor O Neal'd puderself
about. She would hafta stickidall behoinder n gedon withit.
Make a change. It wz all she could do t troy n show tht she wz
really human. The Eleanor O Neale case. So Eleanor wz just
anutha case these days. Thed ad her backwoods n forwoods t
Jamayca loika bleedin pingpong ball; n then thed dropta roight
between th devil n th deep blue sea without a word. Evrybody
tht shid went to when she needid elp'd just changed soids loik
that overnight. Evrything wz black n whoit t them. Th Press.
Th solisituz. Turna. Evrywun'd screwd her owva. Th twofaced
Bastuds. Theyad no roit tuwuv lefta this way loik that. She just
had t pudidall behoinda n gedon with livin outa loif. There wz
nuthin forit, woz th. At thiyend o th day thiyowl thing wz all
just about startin owva.

Billy Watt

DUBBYA DUBBYA

Ethics have been elbowed out
by appetite. Ass-kicking
finger-licking girth instead of brains.
The audience defines itself
in hand-held placards, flashes
of stolen starlight –

                    to the sound
of breaking glass and budding fireworks.
Gear-change chords grind out a beat
while the compere bawls his boxed mic out:
'YEW WANT TAG-TEAM TON-UP? RADICAL RUMBLE?'

Like a well-oiled T. Rex
versus a T-shirted triceratops
the wrestlers make their canvas seismic.
Limber as lumberjacks, lithe
as slung hams in a slaughterhouse,
they slam-dunk each other's skull.
A sunset flip, a bronco buster,
tombstone – now a sharpshooter!
Spine slam, thigh blam, psyched out
powerslam. Up, down, thank you, man.

Those pumped-up babes at ringside,
all big hair and Easter Island tans,
beat down the bad guys from their men,
their rubber sportsbras bicep-taut,
accessories from S and M.
'This is more real than reality,
you retards!' whoops the compere.
Can those waxed red ropes feel warm to him?

Brushing off the candy-shirted refs
the victor, in his sawn-off sweatshirt,
swings through imaginary trees
to perch on the turn-buckle. King
of the ring. The last man standing.

After the show buy the video,
T-shirt, poster or baseball cap;
get Mac, PC or Gameboy format ...
Like an iguana on a rock,
he stomps the flashing darkness
underneath his boots –

                    a human now
evolved into TV at last.

Brian Whittingham

THIS SHIRT

Lies on the ironing board
like it's the creased shirt –
Undisputed Heavyweight Champion of the World.

I'm in quick –
iron setting MAX
auto 20g steam,
skooshing the spray button like a man possessed.

This shirt's surface smiles, melts onto my iron,
I survey the hot wrinkled damage

and like a *second* doing running repairs
I sandpaper the sole-plate,
wipe it clean.

Then, I'm in again –
this time, iron setting MED,
auto 15g steam.

This time I'm ladling in, I'm relentless,
the bit with the buttons
the back
the bit with the buttonholes
the sleeves
the collar …
I stand back exhausted –

then I notice this shirt smirks triumphantly
and when I examine it closer
I see the creases are still there.
Not so pronounced this time, more subtle,
but nevertheless, still there.

It's then I realise this shirt
has once again successfully defended its crown,
and any talk of a re-match at this juncture
would be foolish on my part.

Maybe it's time I thought about hanging up my iron,
and taking stock of my future,
maybe take up a career
as a writer
where crumpled shirts are obligatory.

Jim C. Wilson

LITTLE FOLK

I found an old box in the attic,
left behind by the people before us –
or maybe the people before them.
So, how on earth did it contain
a yellow-and-black cream-cracker tin
identical to yours?
And an Indian carving
just like yours.
And A *Treasury Of Impressionism*
same as the one I bought for you
as a treat in 1983.
And why was there a guide to The Louvre
like the one that sits on our shelf?

And remember the two grey fingers of clay:
she sat slumped in a tiny deckchair
absorbing the darkness, staring hard,
trying to locate the invisible sea;
he, I believe, had been in Belsen
and seemed about to break in two.

I consigned the whole damned lot to the bin
just after you laughed
just after you asked
if the little folk could be us.

BIOGRAPHIES

Mark Baker is a computer design engineer living in Edinburgh, where congealing traffic first made him a motorcyclist and then set him writing. His polemics on bikes as pale green transport have appeared in *The Scotsman* and elsewhere, but these days he mostly writes fiction.

Robert Barton was raised in, and around, mental institutions on the West Coast of Scotland. A troubled youth, he started running from Scotland when still a teenager, spending many years in America. He has now returned to examine the landscape of his formative years. This is his first published work.

Iain Black – studying English at University of Stirling. His work has been published since 1986. *The Jinx* was broadcast on Radio 4 in 1995. His ambition is to have a stage or screenplay produced.

Tom Bryan: born in Canada, 1950. Long-resident in Scotland. Lives in Selkirk, current writing fellow for Scottish Borders. Poet, fiction writer. Widely published, broadcast. First novel *Wolfclaw Chronicles* published in October 2000.

Ron Butlin has published five books of poetry, a collection of short stories, *The Tilting Room*, and two novels, *The Sound of My Voice* and *Night Visits*. His work has been translated into over ten languages. He lives in Edinburgh with his wife and their dog.

Maoilios Caimbeul/Myles Campbell was born in 1944 in Skye, where he now lives. He graduated from Edinburgh University to become a teacher of Gaelic, first in Mull and now in Gairloch. English translations of selected poems appear in the anthology, *An Tuil*, Polygon, 1999.

J.J. Calvin is married, fifty, father of four, and grandfather of four. He took up writing twelve years ago as a hobby. He is chairperson of North Glasgow Writers' Workshop. Two plays he wrote toured the community circuit in Glasgow. He has acted at 'The Fringe' and had a speaking part in *My Name is Joe* (scene was cut).

Stewart Conn's publications include *The Luncheon of the Boating Party* and *Stolen Light: Selected Poems* (both Bloodaxe Books). He lives in Edinburgh.

Ian Crockatt's collection, *Flood Alert*, was published by Chapman in 1996. *Original Myths*, a 14-part poem with etchings by Paul Fleming, was published by Cruachan Publications in May 2000. He is based in Fort William, but works in Aberdeenshire as a Senior Social Worker.

Anna Crowe lives in St Andrews. She works as a tutor for the Open College for the Arts, and as a translator. Her first collection of poetry, *Skating Out of the House*, was published by Peterloo in 1997. Translations in Catalan of poems by her and by Stewart Conn, *Ossa Menor*, were published in October 2000 by Edicions Proa, Barcelona.

Penelopeanne Dalgleish: a native Northamptonian, she arrived in Scotland to study English at St Andrews. Whilst there, she became Britain's only supermarket poet-in-residence. She also married a fellow student and acquired two cats, Lemur and Treacle. A socialist and practising pagan, her work is often controversial.

Robert Davidson is the author of *The Bird and The Monkey* and *Total Immersion*, and editor of *After the Watergaw*. His poem suite, *Columba*, was broadcast on Moray Firth Radio in Spring 2000. He is contributing a series on Highland writers to *Scottish Book Collector* and is Reviews Editor of *Northwords*.

Judy Delin is a member of Stirling Writers' Group. She sees writing as a means of archiving and preserving small moments of emotional significance. She is a lecturer in linguistics and researches in human communication. An academic book, *The Language of Everyday Life*, was published in 2000 by Sage.

Anne Donovan lives in Glasgow. Stories published in various anthologies. Winner of the 1997 Macallan/Scotland on Sunday short story competition and a Canongate prizewinner in 1999. Her collection of short stories is due to be published this spring by Canongate. Currently in receipt of a SAC bursary, she is writing a novel.

Moira Duff was born in Portobello, Edinburgh and now lives in Aberdeen. She has had poems accepted by *London Magazine*, *The Observer* and *Dark Horse*. She is working on her first collection.

Bill Duncan was born in Fife in 1953. His prose and poetry have been published in a range of books and magazines, with work broadcast on radio. His first collection of short fiction, *The Smiling School for Calvinists*, is to be published by Bloomsbury in July 2001.

Matthew Fitt was born in Dundee, 1968. Married to Mirka. Ex-Brownsbank Fellow. Published in *Markings* and *Chapman*. Collections: *Pure Radge* (Akros, 1996), *Sair Heid City* (Kettilonia, 1999). Co-author of *The Grammar Broonie* (SNDA, 2000). First novel: *But n Ben A-Go-Go* (Luath Press, 2000) – a full-length sci-fi adventure written entirely in Scots.

Moira Forsyth's fiction and poetry has appeared in magazines and anthologies. She has also published a short collection of poems, *What the Negative Reveals* (ArtTM 1999), and two novels, *Waiting for Lindsay* (Sceptre 1999) and *David's Sisters* (Sceptre 2000). She was awarded a SAC bursary in 1996.

Pete Fortune lives in Dumfries. Fiction writer in Scots and English. SAC Writers' Bursaries in 1995 and 1999. Co-founder (with Liz Niven) of Watergaw publishers. This is his seventh appearance in *New Writing Scotland*. Collection – *The Hatfields … and others* – looking for a reputable publisher.

Anne C. Frater: born Isle of Lewis in 1967. Native Gaelic speaker. Firs published in *Gairm* magazine (1986). Work has appeared in various magazines and anthologies, and in the collection *Fo 'n t-Slige* (Under the Shell) 1995. Now working at Lews Castle College as a lecturer on the UHI Gaelic degree course.

Valerie Gillies is best-known as the poet who followed both the Tweed and the Tay from source to sea. Her seventh book was published in autumn 2000, a series of portrait studies across Scotland with photographer Rebecca Marr, *Men and Beasts* (Luath).

Rody Gorman – Collections: *Fax* (Polygon 1996); *Cùis-Ghaoil* (diehard 1999); *Bealach Garbh* (Coiscéim 1999) and *On the Underground* (Polygon 2000). Working on collections in English, Irish & Scottish Gaelic; anthologies of 20th century European poetry in Gaelic and of 20th century Irish and Scottish Gaelic poetry; collection of haiku and PhD on Donald MacAulay's poetry. SAC Writing Fellow, Sabhal Mòr Ostaig 1998-2001.

Yvonne Gray is an English teacher and musician living in Orkney with her husband and three sons. Her poems have appeared in *NorthWords*, *Poetry Scotland* and *Rationed Air*, a hand-printed limited edition produced in collaboration with printmaker Carol Dunbar for the 2000 St Magnus Festival exhibition *Artists' Book*.

Robert Green was born and raised in Glasgow, and has recently graduated from the Art School. This is his first published work.

Ian Hunter lives in Carluke. His short stories and poems have appeared in magazines and anthologies in Britain and America. He is currently writer-in-residence with Young Alloa Writers.

Linda Jackson lives and works in Glasgow, She combines working as a lecturer in English and Film with her 'other' life as a musician. After completing a Doctorate in English and Philosophy while having and bringing up her three children, she now writes and edits the literary magazine *Nerve*.

Paula Jennings' poems have appeared in several anthologies, *The Herald* and a number of literary magazines. She won the Democratic Left Poetry Prize in 1995 and was awarded a Scottish Arts Council Writers' Bursary in 1999. She is currently working towards a first collection of poetry.

Helen Lamb – poet and short story writer. A poetry collection, *Strange Fish*, was published by Duende in 1997, and a short story collection, *Superior Bedsits*, will be published by Polygon in Autumn 2001. Her work has also been widely published in anthologies and magazines, and broadcast on BBC Radio 4, Radio Scotland and RTE.

Euan McCulloch was born in 1970 and grew up in the Glasgow area. His first collection *This Time of Day* was published in 1996 by Akros Publications and reprinted in 1998.

Murdo Stal MacDonald (Gaelic patronymic = Murchadh Mhurchaidh Choinnich Mhurchaidh Dòmhnallaich) lives on his native island of Lewis. Some of his poetry has appeared in previous issues of *New Writing Scotland*. 1999 was a dry year for him. He continues to search for The Mangroids.

James McGonigal was born in Dumfries in 1947 and has worked as a teacher and teacher-educator. He has co-edited several anthologies of Scottish writing, most recently *Across the Water: Irishness in Modern Scottish Writing* and *Scottish Religious Poetry*. With Richard Price, he has also published *The Star You Steer By: Basil Bunting and British Modernism*. His own poetry has appeared in various anthologies and in two small press collections: *Unidentified Flying Poems* (1981) and *Driven Home* (1999).

Rob Mackenzie was born in Glasgow in 1964. He is married, plays saxophone and guitar, and has a theology degree from Edinburgh University. He has travelled widely, and works in a housing scheme. He enjoys reading and writing poetry. His work has appeared in various small press publications.

Anne MacLeod's second poetry collection *Just the Caravaggio* appeared from Poetry Salzburg in 1999. Her first, *Standing by Thistles* (Scottish Cultural Press 1997) was shortlisted for a Saltire Award. Her short fiction is published in anthologies from Serpents Tail to HarperCollins. She works as a dermatologist, and has four children.

Ellen McNair was born in Sheffield and lived in numerous places until her family moved to Glasgow when she was nine. She has been writing for years but has only started getting published recently. She now lives in the Derbyshire Peak District and works in higher education.

Iain S Mac a'Phearsain was born and raised on the Canadian prairie in a family of Skye and Islay descent. Educated at universities in Alberta and Nova Scotia he taught French Immersion in high schools before coming to live in Skye where he is a Gaelic lecturer at Sabhal Mòr Ostaig.

John Maley was born in Glasgow in 1962. He has had stories published in *New Writing Scotland*, *Nerve*, and *Across the Water*. Recent screenwriting work includes two short films, *My Daughter's Face* and *Daddy's Girl*. His next film venture is *Fu Manchu and the Socialist Fellowship*.

Andy Manders is from Highland Perthshire. Poet, educator and dad. His work crops up in publications and landscapes across Scotland. First volume of poetry – *the usual holocaust* – due for publication in 2001.

Donald S. Murray comes from the Isle of Lewis and is now an English teacher in Sgoil Lionacleit, Benbecula. His collection of short stories, *Special Deliverance*, was published by Scottish Cultural Press and shortlisted for the Saltire First Books Award. His poetry has also been widely published.

Liz Niven: born Glasgow. Raised in Galloway. Formerly teacher and Scots Language Development Officer for Dumfries and Galloway, currently Writer-in-Residence. Scottish Arts Council Writers' Bursary 1996. Joint runner up McCash Poetry Prize, Glasgow University 1999. Wide range of writing on Scots language in education. Recent publication 'Cree Lines', commissioned poetry in granite/oak/beech/metal for the River Cree in Galloway.

Tom Pow had three books for children published last autumn: *My Dad Was A Cowboy* (Cacafuego press), *Callum's Big Day* (iynx publishing) and *Who Is The World For?* (Walker Books). He lectures in Creative and Cultural Studies at Glasgow University Crichton Campus.

Wayne Price was born in South Wales in 1965 and now lives and teaches in Edinburgh. He has been writing and publishing stories in a variety of journals and anthologies since 1985 and has recently begun work on a second novel.

Sheila Puri: *New Writing Scotland* 15 published a story written by her called *Migrant*. BBC Scotland broadcast *Doors*, which has also been published by *Nomad*. She studied English and Sociology at Hatfield Poly. Recently trained as a counsellor and works with women survivors. She lives in Glasgow with her children and partner.

Olive Ritch was born and brought up in Stromness, Orkney. She now lives in Aberdeen where she works as a social worker. Her writing includes both prose and poetry.

James Robertson is the author of two books of short stories, *Close* (1991) and *The Ragged Man's Complaint* (1993), two collections of poetry, *Sound-Shadow* (1995) and *I Dream of Alfred Hitchcock* (1999) and a novel, *The Fanatic* (2000). He lives in Fife.

April Simmons was born in 1972, and brought up in Cornwall. She has a degree in Law-Chinese Studies from Leeds University, and has worked in publishing in Beijing and Hong Kong. She now lives in Fife.

Kirsty Smith (aka Laura Stevens) is currently working her way through the Scottish education system. She finds the bases for most of her writing there, due to all the colourful and different contrasts of characters a school has to offer. *Mars Bar* is her second published story to date.

Gerry Stewart grew up in the Midwestern United States and moved to Europe at seventeen. She has lived in Norway, Greece and currently Scotland where she has resided on and off since 1991. She is Assistant Editor of Chapman Publishing. She is currently working on her first collection.

Liam Stewart lives in Glasgow. He writes short stories and teaches in F.E. He was joint editor of *The Other Side of the Clyde* and recently edited *Untold Stories: Remembering Clydebank in Wartime*.

Sam Trainor was born in Birmingham in 1972. He is co-director of *bletherink*, Glasgow-based publisher of the annual CD anthology of Scottish performance writers: *Spoke*. He appears regularly on the performance poetry circuit and is currently preparing an avant-garde narrative fiction project, *Zombie*, as a PhD at Glasgow University.

Billy Watt was born in Greenock and now lives in West Lothian, where he works as Principal Teacher of English at Broxburn Academy. He divides his writing time fairly evenly between poetry and fiction.

Brian Whittingham was born and lives in Glasgow. Currently writer in residence for Midlothian and East Lothian districts and poetry editor of *Nerve* magazine. Held writing Fellowship at Yaddo, New York, 1994. Most recent poetry collection, *The Old Man from Brooklyn and the Charing Cross Carpet*, published by Mariscat press, June 2000.

Jim C. Wilson (52) is a poet, who lives in Gullane, East Lothian. He has been Writing Fellow for Stirling District, and won the Hugh MacDiarmid Trophy in 1997. He runs weekly Poetry In Practice sessions at Edinburgh University. Most recent poetry collection: *Cellos in Hell* (Chapman).